STEVE JOBS

E

WHEN THE WORLD TALKS ABOUT MEN WHO ARE KNOWN, ACROSS THE GLOBE, **STEVE JOBS** IS A NAME THAT IS SYNONYMOUS WITH APPLE AND WITH INNOVATION. HE IS A NAME THAT IS KNOWN IN EVERY HOUSEHOLD IN EVERY COUNTRY AND MOST OF US HAVE SOMETHING FROM HIS FAMOUS COMPANY. WE KNOW HIS NAME, BUT WHAT DO WE KNOW ABOUT HIM, THE PERSON? AND HOW HE GOT TO BE *THE* STEVE JOBS?

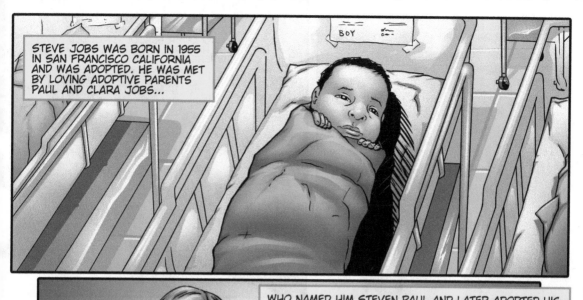

STEVE JOBS WAS BORN IN 1955 IN SAN FRANCISCO CALIFORNIA AND WAS ADOPTED. HE WAS MET BY LOVING ADOPTIVE PARENTS PAUL AND CLARA JOBS...

WHO NAMED HIM STEVEN PAUL AND LATER ADOPTED HIS SISTER PATTI. HE WOULD NOT BE AN ONLY CHILD, EITHER WITH HIS ADOPTIVE FAMILY OR HIS BIRTH PARENTS, AS HIS SISTER, NOVELIST *MONA SIMPSON*, WAS BORN TO HIS BIRTH PARENTS TWO YEARS AFTER HIS BIRTH.

HE LIVED A HAPPILY CHILDHOOD.

HE WENT TO SCHOOL IN CUPERTINO CALIFORNIA AT THE HOMESTEAD HIGH SCHOOL. HE HAD ALWAYS BEEN SMART...

AND BEGAN ATTENDING LECTURES AT *HEWLETT PACKARD* IN PALO ALTO AFTER SCHOOL. IT WOULD BE HIS FIRST STEP TOWARD WHERE HE IS TODAY...

WHEN HE ENTERED INTO A SUMMER EMPLOYMENT, ALONGSIDE *STEVE WOZNIAK*, AT HEWLETT PACKARD. HIS TASTE FOR TECHNOLOGY WOULD GROW EVERY DAY, EVEN WHILE ATTENDING COLLEGE.

STEVE BEGAN TAKING CLASSES AT *REED COLLEGE* IN PORTLAND OREGON, BUT WOULD ONLY STAY FOR A SEMESTER.

HE STAYED ON TO AUDIT CLASSES AT REED, SUCH AS CALLIGRAPHY, WHILE SPENDING TIME AS A POOR COLLEGE STUDENT, GETTING MONEY WHILE RETURNING SODA BOTTLES. HE WOULD LATER MENTION HOW IMPORTANT THAT ONE CLASS WAS TO THE MAC ITSELF, A STRANGE CIRCUMSTANCE INDEED.

BESIDES WORKING AS A TECHNICIAN FOR VIDEO GAME COMPANY *ATARI* IN THE 1970S, STEVE JOBS AND STEVE WOZNIAK FOUND THEMSELVES TOGETHER AGAIN, ATTENDING HOMEBREW COMPUTER CLUB MEETINGS. IT SEEMED LIKE THEY WERE CONNECTED IN SOME WAY...

WHEN BOTH WORKED AT ATARI, JOBS WAS GIVEN THE JOB OF CREATING A CIRCUIT BOARD FOR BREAKOUT, A HIT VIDEO GAME THAT ATARI WAS ATTEMPTING TO TAKE CHIPS OUT OF THE ARCADE MACHINE AND WERE OFFERING $100 FOR EACH CHIP TAKEN OUT.

HE AND WOZNIAK SPLIT THE BONUS BETWEEN THEM, AND FOUND A WAY TO REDUCE THE NUMBER OF CHIPS BY 50, SOMETHING ATARI HAD NO IDEA COULD WORK. THIS WAS THE BEGINNING OF A LONG RELATIONSHIP BETWEEN JOBS AND WOZNIAK, IN SPITE OF JOBS TELLING WOZNIAK THEY WERE ONLY GIVEN $700 AND NOT $5000.

BUT IN 1976, ALONGSIDE WOZNIAK AND *RONALD WAYNE*, AS WELL AS FUNDING FROM *A.C. "MIKE" MARKKULA JR*, STEVE JOBS FOUNDED *APPLE*. AND AS EVERYONE IS AWARE, THE WORLD WOULD BE CHANGED, ALL BECAUSE JOBS CONVINCED WOZNIAK TO ASSEMBLE AND SELL A COMPUTER.

FROM 1978 UNTIL 1983, APPLE HAD SOME TROUBLED YEARS, BUT THEY WOULD COME OUT RELATIVELY UNSCATHED AFTER STEVE MET WITH *JOHN SCULLEY*, CEO OF *PEPSI*, TO GET HIM AS APPLE'S CEO TO MANAGE ITS EXPANSION FROM A SMALL COMPANY INTO SOMETHING MORE.

AND AFTER APPLE'S 1984 SUPER BOWL COMMERCIAL, THEY WOULD IMMEDIATELY BE MORE. THEY'D BE ON EVERYONE'S MINDS. IT WAS ONE OF THE MOST SUCCESSFUL COMMERCIALS TO DATE...

AND IT LEAD TO THE WORLD BEING GIVEN THE *APPLE MACINTOSH COMPUTER*. STEVE JOBS INTRODUCED THE MACINTOSH TO APPLE'S SHAREHOLDERS AT THEIR ANNUAL MEETING AND THE CROWD WENT WILD.

UNFORTUNATELY FOR JOBS, HIS RELATIONSHIP WITH APPLE WOULDN'T LAST IN THE 80'S. AS A SALES SLUMP HIT THE ENTIRE COMPUTER INDUSTRY IN LATE 1984, JOBS AND SCULLEY BEGAN TO GROW LESS AND LESS FRIENDLY. AND BY MAY 1985, SCULLEY LET JOBS GO FROM THE HEAD OF THE MACINTOSH DIVISION. IT WAS A BLOW TO JOBS PERSONALLY AND PROFESSIONALLY.

BUT AS WE WILL SEE AS WE MOVE ALONG, THESE BLOWS DON'T LAST VERY LONG. STEVE MOVED ON SOMEWHAT QUICKLY, FOUNDING ANOTHER COMPUTER COMPANY, *NeXT*.

IT WAS TECHNOLOGICALLY ADVANCED, BUT IT WAS AN EXPENSIVE COMPUTER. THOSE THAT COULD BUY IT, LOVED IT...

AS IT HAD A SOFTWARE DEVELOPMENT SYSTEM THAT WAS ALMOST UNMATCHED IN MOST OTHER COMPUTERS AT THE TIME. IT EVEN HAD A BUILT-IN ETHERNET PORT, SOMETHING COMPLETELY UNHEARD OF AT THE TIME.

AND BECAUSE OF THE TECH THAT THIS COMPUTER HAD, JOBS BEGAN TO MARKET THE COMPUTER TO THE ACADEMIC AND SCIENTIFIC FIELDS. IT WAS A RISKY MOVE, BUT JUST LIKE NeXT, STEVE JOBS WAS ALL ABOUT INNOVATION AND EXPERIMENTATION.

ALONGSIDE HIS WORK WITH NeXT, STEVE CONTINUED TO MOVE FORWARD IN OTHER EXCITING AVENUES. ONE OF THOSE AVENUES WOULD LATER BECOME ONE OF THE MOST INFLUENTIAL GROUPS IN ANIMATED FILMS...

THE GRAPHICS GROUP

ORIGINALLY CALLED THE GRAPHICS GROUP, BUT NOW KNOWN AS *PIXAR*, STEVE PURCHASED THE GROUP FROM *LUCASFILM'S* COMPUTER GRAPHICS DIVISION IN 1986.

FOR THEIR FIRST FEW YEARS OF EXISTENCE, THEY WERE UNSUCCESSFUL AS A COMPANY DEVOTED TO HIGH-END GRAPHICS HARDWARE DEVELOPMENT. THEY ATTEMPTED TO SELL THE PIXAR IMAGE COMPUTER...

BUT THEY WERE UNSUCCESSFUL WITH THAT AS WELL, UP UNTIL THEY STARTED WORKING IN FILMS.

BACK AT HIS OTHER BUSINESS, NeXT WAS WORKING UP WHAT WOULD CHANGE THE WORLD. HIS INTERPERSONAL COMPUTER, AS HE CALLED IT, WOULD ALLOW PEOPLE TO COMMUNICATE AND COLLABORATE TOGETHER IN AN EASY WAY.

HE DEMOED SUCH THINGS AS *NeXTMAIL*, WHICH SUPPORTED UNIVERSALLY VISIBLE, CLICKABLE EMBEDDED GRAPHICS AND AUDIO WITHIN EMAIL WHEN THE REST OF THE WORLD WAS SENDING SIMPLE EMAIL MESSAGES WITH JUST TEXT. STEVE JOBS WAS CHANGING THE WORLD...

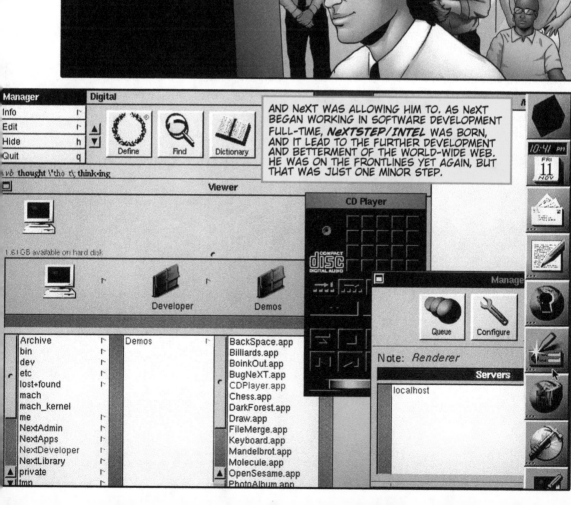

AND NeXT WAS ALLOWING HIM TO. AS NeXT BEGAN WORKING IN SOFTWARE DEVELOPMENT FULL-TIME, *NeXTSTEP/INTEL* WAS BORN, AND IT LEAD TO THE FURTHER DEVELOPMENT AND BETTERMENT OF THE WORLD-WIDE WEB. HE WAS ON THE FRONTLINES YET AGAIN, BUT THAT WAS JUST ONE MINOR STEP.

HIS OTHER PARTNERSHIP, PIXAR, WOULD MAKE A MAJOR SPLASH, BOTH CRITICALLY AND CREATIVELY, WITH THE RELEASE OF *TOY STORY* IN 1995. AS WE ALL KNOW, PIXAR IS A MAJOR NAME IN THE ANIMATED FILM WORLD...

PIXAR WENT ON TO RELEASE SUCH FILMS AS *MONSTERS, INC, WALL-E, THE INCREDIBLES, UP,* AND TWO TOY STORY SEQUELS, AMONG MANY OTHERS. THEY ARE WELL-KNOWN AROUND THE ENTIRE WORLD, JUST LIKE STEVE JOBS AND HIS WORK WITH APPLE COMPUTERS. THERE WOULD BE SPEED BUMPS FOR THE COMPANY OVER THE YEARS, BUT WE'LL GET TO THAT.

IN 1996, STEVE'S COMPANY NeXT WAS PURCHASED BY APPLE FOR $429 MILLION. IT WAS A BOLD MOVE, BRINGING STEVE BACK TO THE COMPANY HE HELPED FOUND, AND ACTUALLY BRINGING HIM BACK AS CEO.

HE OVERSAW THE CREATION OF *MAC OS X*, WHICH INCORPORATED MUCH OF THE TECHNOLOGY FROM NEXTSTEP...

AND HE HELPED GUIDE THE COMPANY TO INCREASED SALES AFTER INTRODUCING SUCH MACHINES AS THE *iMAC*...

AND THE iPOD. BOTH ITEMS WERE CREATED UNDER HIS GUIDANCE AT THE COMPANY, HELPING THEM MOVE TOWARD APPEALING DESIGNS AND POWERFUL BRANDING.

STEVE HELPED THE COMPANY BRANCH OUT, DEVELOPING NEW TECHNOLOGIES AND IMPROVING OTHER DIGITAL APPLIANCES, WHICH HELPED CREATE THE IPOD AND SIMULTANEOUSLY, iTUNES.

APPLE MADE FORAYS INTO CONSUMER ELECTRONICS AND MUSIC DISTRIBUTION BECAUSE OF THE CREATION OF THE IPOD AND *iTUNES*. iTUNES AND THE iTUNES STORE HELPED APPLE GRAB HOLD OF THE MUSIC INDUSTRY AND HELPED THEM MAKE A NAME FOR THEMSELVES IN WAYS VASTLY DIFFERENT FROM THE COMPUTING FIELDS.

BUT AS ALWAYS, STEVE HAD OTHER IRONS IN THE FIRE. IN 2003 AND 2004, PIXAR'S CONTRACT WITH DISNEY WAS NEARING ITS END, AFTER YEARS OF PROFITABILITY FOR BOTH COMPANIES.

UNFORTUNATELY, STEVE JOBS AND MICHAEL EISNER, DISNEY'S CHIEF AT THE TIME, COULD NOT NEGOTIATE A NEW CONTRACT, SO STEVE JOBS ANNOUNCED THAT PIXAR WOULD SEEK A NEW PARTNER ONCE THE CONTRACT WITH DISNEY EXPIRED.

BUT THE EXPIRATION AND THE CLAIM WOULDN'T CHANGE THEIR RELATIONSHIP FOR LONG. AS DISNEY REPLACED MICHAEL EISNER WITH BOB IGER, HE QUICKLY WORKED TO GET PIXAR BACK AT DISNEY.

ON JANUARY 24, 2006, JOBS AND IGER ANNOUNCED THAT DISNEY HAD BOUGHT PIXAR FOR $7.4 BILLION, WHICH ALSO PUT JOBS AS THE LARGEST SINGLE SHAREHOLDER AT DISNEY WITH 7% OF THE COMPANY'S STOCK, MORE THAN ANY OTHER DISNEY EXECUTIVE.

ONCE THE MERGER TOOK PLACE, STEVE JOBS HAD AN IMPORTANT SPOT WITH BOTH DISNEY AND PIXAR. HE JOINED THE BOARD OF DIRECTORS FOR DISNEY AND HAS A SEAT ON A SIX-MAN STEERING COMMITTEE THAT OVERSEES DISNEY AND PIXAR'S COMBINED ANIMATED BUSINESSES. IT IS A ROLE COVETED BY MANY PEOPLE THE WORLD OVER, AND STEVE JOBS HAS IT.

iPhone

IN 2007, APPLE ENTERED THE CELL PHONE BUSINESS WITH THE INTRODUCTION OF THE *iPHONE*, ANOTHER ON A LONG LINE OF NEW TECHNOLOGIES THAT APPLE BUILT UNDER STEVE JOBS. THE iPHONE INCORPORATED TOUCH SCREEN TECHNOLOGY AS WELL AS iPOD CAPABILITIES AND WORKED AS A MOBILE PHONE. IT WAS DIFFERENT AND EXTRAORDINARY, AND THE WORLD NOTICED.

ng the phon

HIS ENTIRE LIFE IS NOT JUST APPLE AND PIXAR AND INVENTIONS THOUGH. HE IS ALSO A DEVOTED HUSBAND AND FATHER, HAVING MARRIED LAURENE POWELL ON MARCH 18, 1991, AND THEY HAVE THREE CHILDREN TOGETHER.

AMONG OTHER THINGS, HE IS HUGE *BEATLES* FAN. HE HAS STATED A NUMBER OF TIMES THAT HIS BUSINESS MODEL IS BASED ON THE BEATLES, THE TOTAL BEING GREATER THAN THE SUM OF THE PARTS. IT IS A MODEL DEVOTED TO THE TEAM, WHICH SHOWS THAT NO MATTER HOW MUCH INNOVATION STEVE JOBS HAS BEEN BEHIND, HE DOESN'T TAKE SOLE CREDIT, NO MATTER WHAT.

BETWEEN THE YEARS OF 1984 AND 1994,
STEVE OWNED A 17,000 SQUARE FOOT, 14
BEDROOM SPANISH COLONIAL MANSION IN
WOODSIDE CALIFORNIA, WHICH STAYED IN AN
ALMOST UNLIVABLE AND UNFINISHED STATE
FOR 10 YEARS WHILE HE LIVED THERE.

STEVE MADE PLANS TO DEMOLISH THE PROPERTY
BUT MET SCRUTINY FROM LOCAL PRESERVATIONISTS
OVER IT. HE WAS GIVEN APPROVAL TO DEMOLISH
THE HOME IN 2004, BUT HE HAD TO ADVERTISE FOR
A YEAR TO SEE IF SOMEONE WOULD BUY AND
RESTORE OR MOVE THE PROPERTY. AFTER A YEAR
AND MANY FALSE STARTS AND STOPS TO SAVE THE
PROPERTY...

AFTER NUMEROUS YEARS AND COURT
ACTIONS AND OVERTURNED DECISIONS,
THE MANSION BEGAN BEING DEMOLISHED
IN FEBRUARY 2011.

IT WAS ANOTHER IN A LONG LINE OF CRITICISMS
THROWN AT STEVE. HE HAS BEEN CRITICIZED FOR
HIS SEEMINGLY ERRATIC AND TEMPERAMENTAL
MANAGEMENT STYLE AND FOR HIS PERSUASION
AND SALESMANSHIP SKILLS.

EVERYTHING FOR STEVE HAS NOT BEEN SUCCESS OR EBBS AND FLOWS THOUGH. IN 2004, STEVE HAD TO ANNOUNCE TO HIS EMPLOYEES AND TEAM MEMBERS AT APPLE THAT HE HAD BEEN DIAGNOSED WITH A *CANCEROUS TUMOR* IN HIS PANCREAS.

HE ORIGINALLY DID NOT WANT TO HAVE SURGERY OR USE MEDICINE FOR THE DISEASE. HE WISHED TO USE A SPECIAL DIET TO DEFEAT THE DISEASE, BUT IN JULY OF 2004, HE UNDERWENT A WHIPPLE PROCEDURE WHICH SUCCESSFULLY REMOVED THE TUMOR.

EVEN IN ILLNESS, STEVE IS A SUCCESS. PANCREATIC CANCER IS USUALLY SOMETHING THAT IS ALMOST IMPOSSIBLE TO DEFEAT, BUT STEVE CAME OUT ON TOP.

BUT ONE THING HE COULDN'T DEFEAT WAS THE CONSTANT QUESTIONING. IN 2006, GIVING THE KEYNOTE SPEECH FOR APPLE'S ANNUAL WORLDWIDE DEVELOPERS CONFERENCE, HE WAS THOUGHT TO BE GAUNT AND LISTLESS, AND HIS HEALTH WAS QUESTIONED.

MORE CONCERNS AROSE IN 2008 AND APPLE WAS FORCED TO STATE THAT THE MATTERS WERE PRIVATE, WHICH INDEED, THEY WERE. IT DIDN'T STOP THE MEDIA FROM GOING CRAZY THOUGH...

IN 2008, *BLOOMBERG* MISTAKENLY ANNOUNCED HIS DEATH IN AN OBITUARY, PUBLISHING A 2500 WORD OBITUARY BUT LEAVING HIS AGE AND CAUSE OF DEATH BLANK. NUMEROUS OTHER SOURCES REPORTED ON THIS, CAUSING STEVE TO MAKE A FEW COMMENTS ABOUT HIS "DEATH" AT PRESENTATIONS AND MEDIA EVENTS.

HE WOULD GO BACK AND FORTH WITH APPLE, GIVING KEYNOTE SPEECHES WHEN HE WAS ABLE TO, BUT ALSO FIGHTING WITH HEALTH ISSUES FROM TIME TO TIME AND BEING FORCED TO TAKE TIME AWAY...

HE HAS BEEN FORCED TO TAKE TIME FOR HORMONE IMBALANCE, COMPLEX HEALTH ISSUES THAT WOULD NEVER BE DIVULGED IN FULL, AND HE HAS EVEN HAD A LIVER TRANSPLANT DUE TO THESE ONGOING HEALTH ISSUES.

Team,

At my request, the board of directors ⬛ medical leave of absence so I can focus on my health. I will continue as CEO and b ⬛ strategic decisions for the company.

I have asked Tim Cook to be resp ⬛ s day to day operations. I have great confidence that Tim and the rest ⬛ ement team will do a terrific job executing the exciting plans we have in place f ⬛

⬛ can. In the meantime, my family and I would

I love Apple so much and ho ⬛ deeply appreciate respect f ⬛

Steve

A YEAR AND A HALF AFTER HE RETURNED FROM THE LIVER TRANSPLANT, HE ANNOUNCED HIS LEAVE OF ABSENCE TO FOCUS ON HIS HEALTH TO HIS EMPLOYEES, BUT HE WOULD CONTINUE TO MAKE AND BE INVOLVED IN STRATEGIC COMPANY DECISIONS. HE WOULD NOT BE AWAY FROM THE COMPANY IN ALL ASPECTS, JUST DAY-TO-DAY.

HIS LIFE HAS BEEN MET WITH MANY SUCCESSES, AND THOSE SUCCESSES HAVE COME WITH GREAT REWARD FOR STEVE. BESIDES HIS MASSIVE WEALTH, HE HAS BEEN AWARDED SUCH ITEMS AS THE *NATIONAL MEDAL OF TECHNOLOGY*, THE *JEFFERSON AWARD FOR PUBLIC SERVICE*, AND HE'S BEEN NAMED ONE OF THE MOST POWERFUL PEOPLE IN THE WORLD AND IN BUSINESS BY *FORBES MAGAZINE* AS WELL AS BEING INDUCTED INTO CALIFORNIA'S HALL OF FAME BY GOVERNOR ARNOLD SCHWARZENEGGER.

HE IS KNOWN ALL OVER THE WORLD. AND
BECAUSE OF WHO HE IS AND WHAT HE HAS
DONE FOR TECHNOLOGY, HE HAS BEEN
PARODIED OR SHOWN IN FILMS AND TV.
THERE WERE 2 *DOCUMENTARY* FILMS ABOUT
THE RISE OF THE PERSONAL COMPUTER AND
THE INTERNET THAT DEALT WITH JOBS IN
DEPTH, AS WELL AS TV MOVIE CALLED
PIRATES OF SILICON VALLEY WHICH DEALT
WITH THE RISE OF APPLE AND *MICROSOFT* IN
WHICH HE WAS PLAYED BY ER'S NOAH WYLE.
HE HAS ALSO BEEN PARODIED ON SUCH
SHOWS AS *30 ROCK, THE SIMPSON'S,
SATURDAY NIGHT LIVE,* AND *MAD TV.*

THE RICHEST PEOPLE IN AMI

Forbe

400

STEVE CURRENTLY HOLDS 5.426 MILLION SHARES OF APPLE, AS WELL AS 138 MILLION SHARES OF DISNEY WHICH HE RECEIVED ONCE DISNEY ACQUIRED PIXAR. HE HAS BEEN LISTED AS THE 43RD *WEALTHIEST AMERICAN* BY FORBES MAGAZINE WHO ESTIMATED HIS WEALTH AT $5.1 BILLION. MOST OF HIS SUCCESS AND HIS WEALTH CAN BE ATTRIBUTED TO HIS SALESMANSHIP AND HIS AGGRESSIVE AND DEMANDING TENDENCIES. IT HAS HELPED APPLE SET TRENDS AND KEEP INNOVATIVE AND IN STYLE, SOMETHING THAT HAS CARRIED FROM APPLE TO PIXAR AS WELL.

BILLIONAIRES

STEVE JOBS

BILL GATES

WARREN BUFFET

8/4/2011 $ 5,100,000,000

DOLLARS

+ 00/100

steven jobs

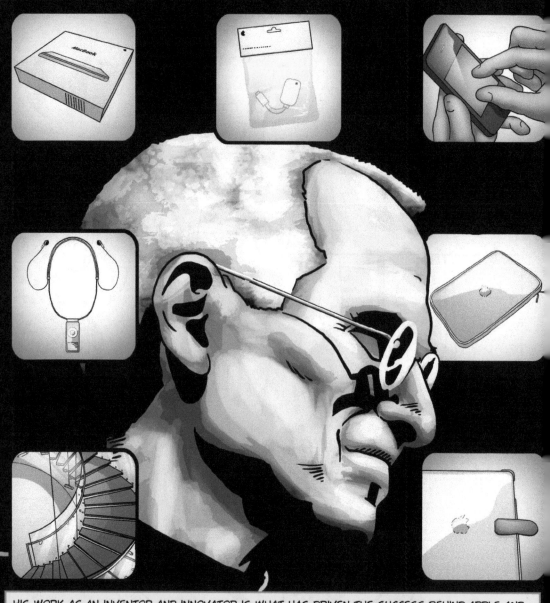

HIS WORK AS AN INVENTOR AND INNOVATOR IS WHAT HAS DRIVEN THE SUCCESS BEHIND APPLE AND PIXAR. HE IS SEEN AS THE INVENTOR OR CO-INVENTOR OF MORE THAN 230 PATENTS OR PATENT APPLICATIONS DEALING WITH COMPUTER AND PORTABLE DEVICE TECHNOLOGIES. THERE ARE WAY TOO MANY TO LIST AND MORE THAN ANY OF US WOULD EVEN BELIEVE, BUT HE HAS BEEN ON THE FRONTLINE OF INNOVATION SINCE HE BEGAN WORK ON THE FIRST APPLE COMPUTER.

IN SPITE OF TWO MORE MAJOR APPEARANCES IN JUNE, HIS FAILING HEALTH AND CONCERNS OVER CONTINUED TROUBLE, HE ANNOUNCED HIS *RESIGNATION* FROM APPLE. THE ANNOUNCEMENT CAME ON AUGUST 24, 2011, AND WAS QUICKLY FOLLOWED BY APPLE PROMISING THAT THEY WOULD CONTINUE TO INNOVATE AND CREATE IN THE SPIRIT OF STEVE JOBS. STEVE JOBS' PRESENCE WILL BE FELT AT APPLE *FOREVER*, IN SPITE OF HIS STEPPING DOWN AS CEO.

ON OCTOBER 5, 2011, STEVE JOBS PASSED AWAY. NO ONE WILL EVER DENY THAT HE CHANGED THE FACE OF TECHNOLOGY AND ELECTRONICS FOREVER. HIS MARK WILL INDELIBLY BE FELT FOR YEARS TO COME, WHETHER ON PHONES, COMPUTERS, MUSIC SERVICES, OR IN MOVIES. HE'LL NEVER BE FORGOTTEN.

HE WAS A VISIONARY, A DEDICATED WORKER AND A DEDICATED THINKER. HE WAS ALWAYS AT THE FOREFRONT OF TECH, MAKING EASY TO USE AND EXCITING GADGETS THAT PEOPLE NOT ONLY WANTED TO HAVE BUT WANTED TO SHOW OFF. HE MADE TECH BOTH SEXY AND SOPHISTICATED, AND HE DID EVERYTHING HE COULD TO LEAVE HIS STAMP ON EVERYTHING HE TOUCHED.

AND THAT IS ALL WE COULD ASK FOR. STEVE JOBS HAS LEFT THIS WORLD, BUT HE WON'T SOON BE FORGOTTEN.

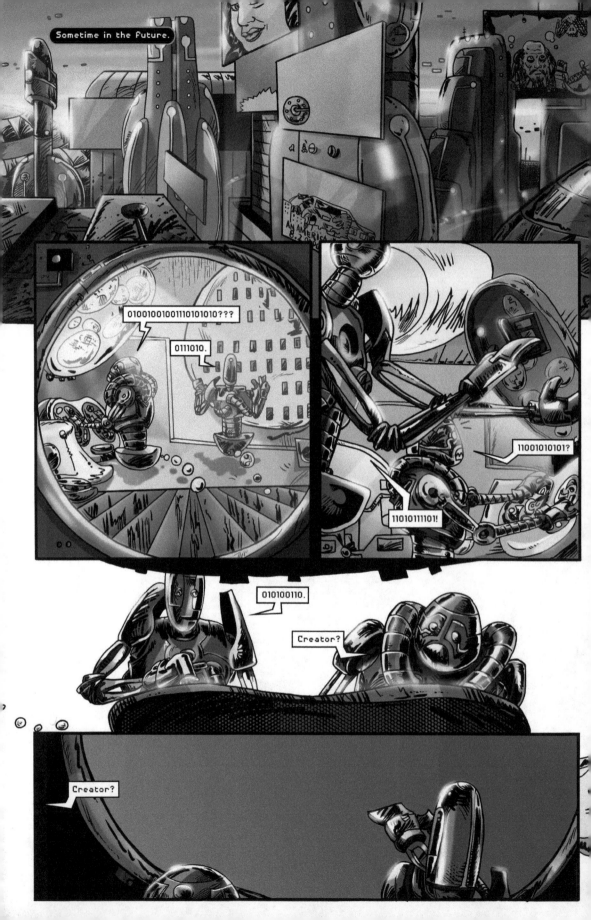

DATA PACKAGE LOADING

TRANSFERRING TO CENTRALWORLD
LIBRARY

BEGIN PRESENTATION...

1955 WOULD ALSO SEE THE BIRTH OF ANOTHER SORT... IT WAS THE SAME YEAR THAT IBM WOULD RELEASE THEIR SERIES 702. IT WOULD BE A MAJOR STEPPING STONE FOR IBM AND COMPUTER PROCESSING IN GENERAL.

THE YEAR WAS 1955 AND ON OCTOBER 28TH WILLIAM H GATES SR. AND MARY GATES WELCOMED THEIR SON INTO THE WORLD. WILLIAM H GATES III WAS BORN AT THE SWEDISH HOSPITAL IN SEATTLE, WASHINGTON.

GROWING UP, BILL (OR TREY AS HIS FAMILY WOULD CALL HIM) WAS INTELLIGENT. HE WAS ALSO HIGHLY COMPETITIVE AND WOULD OFTEN CHALLENGE HIS OLDER SISTER TO CARDS AND BOARD GAMES SUCH AS RISK AND MONOPOLY.

OK, I'LL LET YOU PASS WITHOUT HAVING TO PAY, BUT I WANT YOUR RAILROAD.

WHAT?

WILLIAM (OR BILL AS THE WORLD WOULD LATER KNOW HIM) WAS THE COUPLE'S SECOND CHILD. HE WOULD BE BORN WITH AN OLDER SISTER KRISTI AND LATER A YOUNGER SISTER LIBBY WOULD BE ADDED TO THE FAMILY.

MONOPOLY

IN 1962 THE WORLD'S FAIR CAME TO SEATTLE AND THE GATES FAMILY WAS EAGER TO SEE ALL THE WONDERS AND SITES OF THE FAIR WHICH WAS ALSO KNOWN AS THE CENTURY 21 EXPOSITION.

THE US WAS IN THE THROWS OF THE "SPACE RACE" AND WAS PROUDLY DISPLAYING THE CUTTING EDGE TECHNOLOGY OF THE DAY AND DEMONSTRATING HOW THE FUTURE WOULD BE A BETTER PLACE THANKS TO AMERICAN INGENUITY. BILL WAS STRUCK BY THIS VISION OF THE FUTURE WHERE COMPUTERS WERE INTEGRATED INTO OUR LIVES.

BILL QUICKLY FIT IN AT LAKESIDE AND EXCELLED IN MATHEMATICS. HE ALSO TOOK AN INTEREST IN DRAMA AND BECAME VERY COMFORTABLE ON STAGE.

FIVE YEARS EARLIER THE TELETYPE CORPORATION INTRODUCED THE ARS-33 TELEPRINTER. IT WAS AN AFFORDABLE PRINTING TERMINAL THAT USED A PAPER TAPE PUNCH AND READER TO STORE AND READ DATA.

THE LAKESIDE SCHOOL'S MOTHERS CLUB USED PROFITS FROM A RUMMAGE SALE TO PURCHASE ONE FOR THE SCHOOL ALONG WITH A BLOCK OF TIME ON A GE COMPUTER.

THE ARS-33 PROVIDED BILL WITH HIS FIRST CONTACT WITH COMPUTERS AND PROGRAMMING. THE INTELLIGENT AND CURIOUS BOY WAS FASCINATED WITH THE LIMITLESS POSSIBILITIES.

BILL WOULD BEFRIEND AN UPPERCLASSMAN NAMED PAUL ALLEN. THE TWO WERE THE EXACT OPPOSITES IN THAT PAUL WAS SHY AND QUITE AND BILL WAS BOISTEROUS AND OCCASIONALLY CONFRONTATIONAL. BUT THEY SHARED A COMMON CURIOSITY AND INTEREST IN THE FUTURE THAT WAS POSSIBLE THROUGH COMPUTERS.

BILL ALONG WITH PAUL WOULD SNEAK OUT AT NIGHT TO WORK ON THE MACHINE AFTER HOURS. SOMETIMES THE TWO WOULD FIGHT BUT BOTH KNEW THEY NEEDED EACH OTHER AND TOGETHER THEY CREATED SIMPLE PROGRAMS - IT WAS PROOF THAT THEY WERE ON TO SOMETHING.

BECAUSE OF THEIR EARLY SUCCESS, THE TWO BOYS STARTED A BUSINESS TOGETHER WHEN BILL WAS ONLY 15. THEY PRODUCED A PROGRAM THAT WOULD HELP TRACK THE FLOW OF TRAFFIC IN SEATTLE AND EARNED TWENTY THOUSAND DOLLARS IN THE PROCESS. COMPUTERS HAD BECOME A SERIOUS BUSINESS TO THE BOYS.

IN 1972 REALITY SET IN AND BILL HAD TO SHIFT HIS FOCUS BACK ON THE CAREER HIS PARENTS PREFERRED. HE HEADED OFF TO WASHINGTON DC TO INTERN AS A SENATE PAGE.

UPON GRADUATION FROM LAKESIDE BILL WAS ACCEPTED INTO HARVARD, MUCH TO HIS PARENT'S SATISFACTION. THERE HE CONTINUED THE PATH TOWARDS A FUTURE IN LAW BUT IT WAS CLEAR HE HAD NO PASSION FOR HIS STUDIES. HE MANAGED TO STAY ACTIVE BY SPENDING MOST OF HIS FREE TIME IN THE SCHOOLS COMPUTER CENTER... SELDOM SLEEPING.

BILL MADE SOME GOOD FRIENDS AT HARVARD, AND TO SATISFY HIS COMPETITIVE NATURE HE WOULD OFTEN PLAY POKER WITH THEM. FOR ALL OF HIS ACTIVITIES, HE NEVER FOUND TIME FOR A REAL RELATIONSHIP AND WOULD PUSH WOMAN AWAY, ALWAYS FEELING THEY WERE NOT A GOOD MATCH FOR HIM INTELLECTUALLY.

BILL GATES OLD FRIEND PAUL ALLEN HAD DROPPED OUT OF THE UNIVERSITY OF WASHINGTON AND MOVED TO BOSTON TO TAKE A JOB AS A PROGRAMMER FOR HONEYWELL. ONE DAY ALLEN STUMBLED UPON A MAGAZINE ANNOUNCING THE FIRST EVER MINI-COMPUTER...

... THE ALTAIR 8800 FROM MITS. HE IMMEDIATELY THOUGHT OF HIS OLD FRIEND BILL.

ALLEN AND GATES REUNITED AND CONVINCED MITS THAT THEY COULD WRITE A BASIC PROGRAM LANGUAGE FOR THE MACHINE. AFTER TWO MONTHS OF TIRELESS WORK IN THE HARVARD COMPUTER CENTER, ALLEN FLEW TO NEW MEXICO TO SHOW ED ROBERTS OF MITS WHAT THEY HAD CREATED.

ROBERTS WAS HIGHLY IMPRESSED BY WHAT GATES WOULD LATER REFER TO AS "THE COOLEST CODE I EVER WROTE". IT WAS A BASIC LANGUAGE INTERPRETER THAT PRODUCED A SIMPLE MATHEMATICAL EQUATION, BUT HISTORIC NONE THE LESS.

1975 ALLEN AND GATES FORMED A COMPANY THAT WOULD START SMALL BUT GROW FURTHER THAN ANYONE AT THE TIME COULD IMAGINE... THEY CALLED IT MICROSOFT.

MUCH TO HIS MOTHER'S DISMAY, BILL GATES DROPPED OUT OF HARVARD AND JOINED PAUL ALLEN IN ALBUQUERQUE, NEW MEXICO WHERE MICROSOFT WOULD BE BASED FIRST.

IN THE SOFTWARE WORLD OF THAT DAY, MOST PEOPLE JUST SWIPED CODE WITHOUT PAYING FOR IT. THIS WAS SOMETHING BILL GATES DIDN'T LIKE. HE FELT THAT IF HE WORKED HARD DEVELOPING A PROGRAM, HE SHOULD BE PAID FOR HIS TIME BY EVERYONE WHO USED IT. THOUGH HE WAS SEEN AS AN OUTSIDER BECAUSE OF THIS VERY PUBLIC STANCE, IN THE YEARS THAT WOULD FOLLOW HE WOULD BE PROVEN RIGHT.

AFTER A BREAK UP WITH MITS, MICROSOFT EXPANDED INTO OTHER COMPUTER LANGUAGES INCLUDING COBOL, FORTRAN AND PASCAL. THEY ALSO BEGAN TO SELL TO OTHER COMPUTER COMPANIES WHERE THEIR PRODUCTS WERE USED ON MACHINES LIKE THE TRS-80 AND THE APPLE II. IN 1978 WITH 13 EMPLOYEES, GATES AND ALLEN DECIDED TO MOVE THE COMPANY BACK TO SEATTLE WHERE IT ALL BEGAN. THIS MOVE OCCURRED JUST AS THEIR YEAR-END SALES FIGURES CAME IN AT OVER A MILLION DOLLARS.

BILL BECAME THE "FACE" OF MICROSOFT IN ADVERTISEMENTS AND ON THE ROAD. HE BECAME A PROMOTIONAL FORCE TO BE RECKONED WITH WHEN MEETING WITH NEW CLIENTS.

BEING BACK HOME IN SEATTLE ALSO BROUGHT BILL BACK TO HIS BELOVED MOTHER. AT THIS TIME MARY GATES WAS HEAVILY INVOLVED WITH THE UNITED WAY AND SAT ON THE BOARD ALONG WITH THE CEO OF IBM, JOHN OPEL. MARY MADE SURE SHE TOLD JOHN ABOUT HER SON AND HIS COMPANY.

IBM APPROACHED MICROSOFT ABOUT DEVELOPING AN OPERATING SYSTEM FOR THEIR NEW LINE OF HOME PCS. FACED WITH DEVELOPING SOMETHING FROM SCRATCH, GATES OPTED INSTEAD TO BUY A SYSTEM CALLED Q-DOS FROM TIM PATTERSON FOR $75,000. IN 1982 IBM SHIPPED PCS WITH A MODIFIED VERSION CALLED MSDOS 1.0.

BILL GATES PROVED TO BE AN AMAZING BUSINESSMAN. WHEN HE NEGOTIATED THE COPYRIGHTS OF MS-DOS TO IBM, HE KEPT THE RIGHTS TO THE SOURCE CODE. WHAT THIS MEANT WAS THAT AS NEW COMPUTER MANUFACTURES CAME UP, GATES AND ALLEN WHERE FREE TO SELL THIS CODE TO THEM AS WELL.

1983 WAS ALSO THE YEAR THAT PAUL ALLEN, BILL'S FRIEND AND BUSINESS PARTNER WAS DIAGNOSED WITH HODGKIN'S DISEASE. ALLEN STEPPED DOWN FROM MICROSOFT TO UNDERGO EXTENSIVE RADIATION TREATMENT.

THOUGH ALLEN WOULD ULTIMATELY SURVIVE AND HIS CANCER WOULD GO INTO REMISSION, AT 28 BILL GATES WAS LEFT ALONE TO RUN THE MULTI-MILLION DOLLAR COMPANY THAT HE AND HIS HIGH-SCHOOL FRIEND HAD STARTED. IT SHOOK THE NORMALLY FOCUSED AND DRIVEN GATES, AND HE KNEW THAT THINGS WOULD NEVER BE THE SAME FOR HIM OR MICROSOFT.

BY 1983 MICROSOFT HAD OVER A HUNDRED EMPLOYEES AND WAS BRINGING IN REVENUE IN EXCESS OF 16 MILLION DOLLARS, MOSTLY DUE TO THE FACT THAT OVER 30% OF ALL COMPUTERS WERE RUNNING MICROSOFT SOFTWARE.

NOVEMBER 20TH 1985 SAW THE RELEASE OF THE VERSION WINDOWS AND COMPUTERS WOULD BE CHANGED FOR GENERATIONS. VERSION 1.0 CAME OUT OF YEARS OF DEVELOPMENT THAT STARTED IN 1981 WHEN IT WAS KNOWN AS INTERFACE MANAGER.

TO DREAM THE IMPOSSIBLE DREAM ... ♪

IT WAS A SLOW BUILD FOR WINDOWS AND WOULD CREATE A BIT OF CONTROVERSY WHEN APPLE POINTED OUT THAT IT CLOSELY RESEMBLED THE MACINTOSH OPERATING SYSTEM. THE TWO WOULD END UP IN COURT BUT MICROSOFT WOULD PREVAIL.

IN 1986 RIDING THE PUBLICITY OF THE WINDOWS LAUNCH, BILL GATES TOOK HIS COMPANY PUBLIC. ON MARCH 14TH PEOPLE COULD FOR THE FIRST TIME BUY STOCK IN MICROSOFT FOR TWENTY-ONE DOLLARS A SHARE. GATES PERSONALLY HELD 48% OF THE STOCK MAKING HIM A 31 YEAR OLD BILLIONAIRE.

1987 WOULD SEE THE LAUNCH OF WINDOWS 2.0, A SOMEWHAT IMPROVED VERSION OF MICROSOFT'S CORNERSTONE PRODUCT AND THIS WOULD SHIP WITH ALL NEW BUILTIN FEATURES. THOUGH SUCCESSFUL, OTHER SYSTEMS WERE MUCH MORE POPULAR WITH THE AVERAGE COMPUTER USER.

IN 1987 MELINDA FRENCH GRADUATED WITH AN MBA FROM DUKE UNIVERSITY AND THAT SAME YEAR SHE JOINED MICROSOFT AS A PRODUCT MANAGER. WHILE IN THIS POSITION SHE WOULD BE INSTRUMENTAL IN THE LAUNCHING OF SEVERAL MICROSOFT PRODUCTS INCLUDING PUBLISHER.

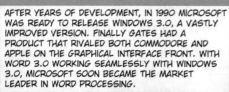

AFTER YEARS OF DEVELOPMENT, IN 1990 MICROSOFT WAS READY TO RELEASE WINDOWS 3.0, A VASTLY IMPROVED VERSION. FINALLY GATES HAD A PRODUCT THAT RIVALED BOTH COMMODORE AND APPLE ON THE GRAPHICAL INTERFACE FRONT. WITH WORD 3.0 WORKING SEAMLESSLY WITH WINDOWS 3.0, MICROSOFT SOON BECAME THE MARKET LEADER IN WORD PROCESSING.

TODAY WE'RE INTRODUCING MICROSOFT WINDOWS VERSION THREE.

THE EARLY 90S WOULD FIND GATES CONSTANTLY DEFENDING HIMSELF AND MICROSOFT FROM THE FTC AND OTHER OUTSIDE FORCES TRYING TO BRING DOWN MICROSOFT.

THROUGHOUT THIS TIME BILL WAS BEING SEEN MORE AND MORE WITH MELINDA FRENCH, AND THE TWO BONDED ON A LEVEL THAT TOOK BILL BY SURPRISE. HE HAD FINALLY FOUND THAT SPECIAL PERSON WHOM HE CONNECTED WITH INTELLECTUALLY AND EMOTIONALLY.

IN 1993 BILL GATES WAS INVITED TO WASHINGTON ONCE AGAIN, NOT TO BE A SENATE PAGE AND NOT TO DEFEND HIS COMPANY AGAINST CHARGES OF BEING A MONOPOLY, BUT TO MEET THE PRESIDENT OF THE UNITED STATES. BILL GATES WAS AWARDED THE PRESTIGIOUS NATIONAL MEDAL OF TECHNOLOGY BY PRESIDENT BUSH.

AT THE END OF THAT SAME YEAR THE ENTIRE GATES FAMILY TOOK A TRIP TO HAWAII FOR A CELEBRATION, THE WEDDING OF BILL AND MELINDA. BILL WAS FINALLY READY TO SETTLE DOWN, HE HAD FOUND HIS SOUL MATE.

ON JANUARY 1ST 1994 BILL AND MELINDA GATES WERE MARRIED ON THE SMALL ISLAND OF LANAI IN A SEASIDE CEREMONY. GATES OLD HARVARD BUDDY AND MICROSOFT EXECUTIVE STEVE BALLMER WAS THE BEST MAN AND GOOD FRIENDS WARREN BUFFET AND PAUL ALLEN WERE IN ATTENDANCE. AFTER A HONEYMOON IN FIJI, BILL RETURNED TO WORK RENEWED AND HAPPY, BUT SADLY THAT SENSE OF EUPHORIA WOULD NOT LAST ...

... ON JUNE 10TH 1994 MARY GATES ...
BILLS MOTHER AND STRONGEST SUPPORTER
PASSED AWAY, A VICTIM OF BREAST CANCER.
BILL WAS HEARTBROKEN.

IN 1996 BILL WOULD BE DECLARED THE WEALTHIEST MAN IN THE WORLD BUT THIS NEWS MEANT NOTHING TO HIM NEXT TO THE BIRTH OF HIS FIRST CHILD JENNIFER GATES, BORN APRIL 26. BILL FINALLY HAD A FAMILY.

1997 WOULD FIND BILL AND MELINDA MOVING TO A BEAUTIFUL NEW HOME OVER LOOKING LAKE WASHINGTON. THE MASSIVE SIXTY SIX THOUSAND SQUARE FOOT HOME COST WELL OVER NINETY MILLION DOLLARS TO CONSTRUCT.

AS TESTAMENT TO BILL'S LOVE OF READING AND KNOWLEDGE, HIS HOME FEATURES A LIBRARY THAT HOUSES ONE OF HIS MOST PRIZED POSSESSIONS - THE FAMED DAVINCI NOTEBOOK THAT HE PAID OVER THIRTY MILLION DOLLARS TO OWN.

THOUGH NO BUSINESS IS DONE IN THIS HOUSE, BILL'S VISION OF THE FUTURE IS CLEAR THROUGHOUT. THE HOUSE FEATURES AN ELABORATE COMPUTER CONTROL SYSTEM THAT HARKENS BACK TO THE DISPLAYS HE SAW AT THE WORLD'S FAIR IN 1962.

IT WAS QUICKLY BECOMING OBVIOUS TO GATES AND BALLMER THAT THE INTERNET WAS THE NEXT FRONTIER FOR COMPUTING AND PERHAPS THEY WERE FAILING TO TAKE MICROSOFT INTO THIS REALM FAST ENOUGH. BY 1997 NETSCAPE WAS QUICKLY BECOMING THE STANDARD WEB BROWSING SOFTWARE AND BILL KNEW IT WAS TIME TO MAKE HIS MOVE.

IN THE MONTHS LEADING UP TO THE LAUNCH OF WINDOWS 98, MICROSOFT MADE A MOVE TO POSITION ITS BROWSER INTERNET EXPLORER AS THE NEW STANDARD BY ADDING IT TO THE WINDOWS BUNDLE. THIS WAS A SMART BUSINESS MOVE, BUT IT WOULD BRING GATES BACK INTO COURT TO DEFEND HIS COMPANY ONCE AGAIN.

THAT MUST BE WHY WE'RE NOT SHIPPING WINDOWS 98 YET?

WHILE DEFENDING HIS COMPANY GATES MOVED FORWARD, BUT FOUND EGG ON HIS FACE WHEN A DEMONSTRATION OF WINDOWS 98 AT THE COMDEX EXPO SAW THE SYSTEM CRASH. AS WITH MOST THINGS, GATES DIDN'T MISS A BEAT AND MANAGED TO QUICKLY RECOVER.

BUT WINDOWS 98 DID SHIP IN JUNE OF 1998 AND JOINED ITS PREDECESSORS AS THE MOST POPULAR OPERATING SYSTEM OF THE DAY. IT WOULD FEATURE MANY GRAPHICAL AND PERFORMANCE ENHANCEMENTS, BUT MOST NOTABLE WERE THE ADDITIONS OF INTERNET BASED PROGRAMS SUCH AS OUTLOOK EXPRESS, FRONT PAGE EXPRESS, MICROSOFT CHAT AND INTERNET EXPLORER 4.0.1.

THE FOLLOWING YEAR GATES WOULD BECOME A FATHER AGAIN. HIS SON RORY JOHN GATES WAS BORN.

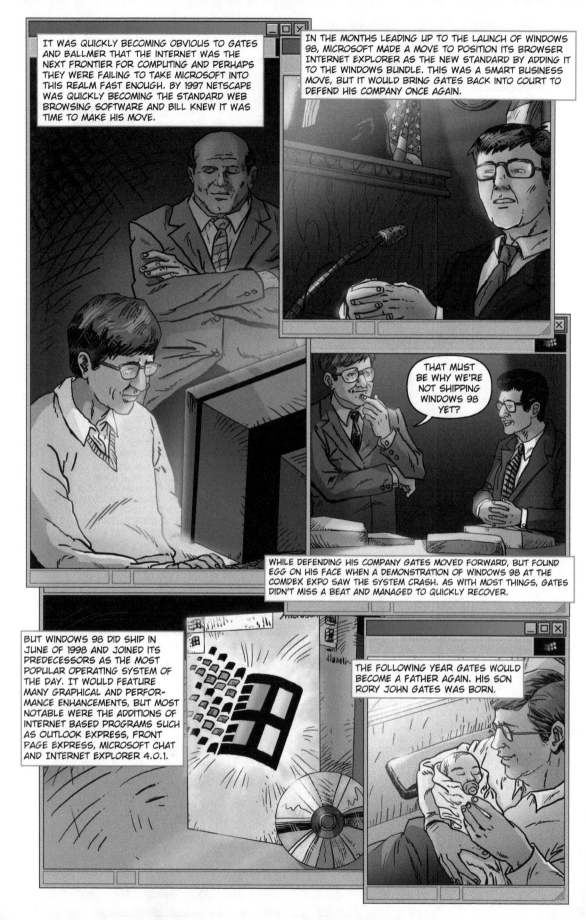

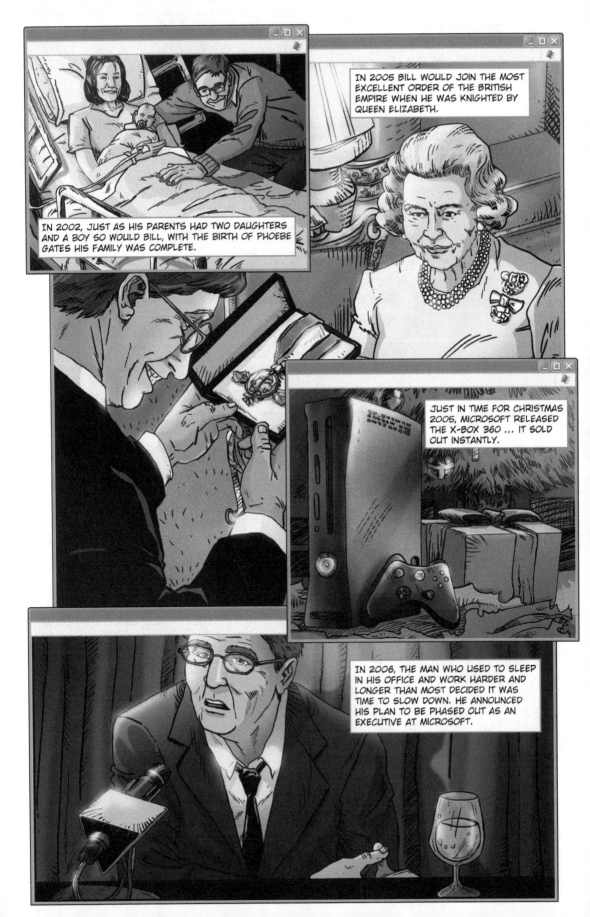

IN 2005 BILL WOULD JOIN THE MOST EXCELLENT ORDER OF THE BRITISH EMPIRE WHEN HE WAS KNIGHTED BY QUEEN ELIZABETH.

IN 2002, JUST AS HIS PARENTS HAD TWO DAUGHTERS AND A BOY SO WOULD BILL, WITH THE BIRTH OF PHOEBE GATES HIS FAMILY WAS COMPLETE.

JUST IN TIME FOR CHRISTMAS 2005, MICROSOFT RELEASED THE X-BOX 360 ... IT SOLD OUT INSTANTLY.

IN 2006, THE MAN WHO USED TO SLEEP IN HIS OFFICE AND WORK HARDER AND LONGER THAN MOST DECIDED IT WAS TIME TO SLOW DOWN. HE ANNOUNCED HIS PLAN TO BE PHASED OUT AS AN EXECUTIVE AT MICROSOFT.

BEFORE HE WOULD STEP DOWN HE WOULD OVERSEE THE LAUNCH OF WINDOWS VISTA, AND FINALLY HE GRADUATED FROM HARVARD ACCEPTING AN HONORARY DEGREE FROM HIS OLD SCHOOL.

I'VE BEEN WAITING MORE THAN THIRTY YEARS TO SAY THIS, "DAD, I ALWAYS TOLD YOU I WOULD COME BACK AND GET MY DEGREE".

...HUMANITY'S GREATEST ADVANCES ARE NOT IN ITS DISCOVERIES - BUT IN HOW THOSE DISCOVERIES ARE APPLIED TO REDUCE INEQUITY. WHETHER THROUGH DEMOCRACY, STRONG PUBLIC EDUCATION, QUALITY HEALTH CARE, OR BROAD ECONOMIC OPPORTUNITY - REDUCING INEQUITY IS THE HIGHEST HUMAN ACHIEVEMENT.

IF WE CAN FIND APPROACHES THAT MEET THE NEEDS OF THE POOR IN WAYS THAT GENERATE PROFITS FOR BUSINESS AND VOTES FOR POLITICIANS, WE WILL HAVE FOUND A SUSTAINABLE WAY TO REDUCE INEQUITY IN THE WORLD.

THIS TASK IS OPEN-ENDED. IT CAN NEVER BE FINISHED. BUT A CONSCIOUS EFFORT TO ANSWER THIS CHALLENGE WILL CHANGE THE WORLD.

I AM OPTIMISTIC THAT WE CAN DO THIS, BUT I TALK TO SKEPTICS WHO CLAIM THERE IS NO HOPE. THEY SAY: "INEQUITY HAS BEEN WITH US SINCE THE BEGINNING, AND WILL BE WITH US TILL THE END - BECAUSE PEOPLE JUST ... DON'T ... CARE."

I COMPLETELY DISAGREE. I BELIEVE WE HAVE MORE CARING THAN WE KNOW WHAT TO DO WITH.

YOU GRADUATES ARE COMING OF AGE IN AN AMAZING TIME. AS YOU LEAVE HARVARD, YOU HAVE TECHNOLOGY THAT MEMBERS OF MY CLASS NEVER HAD. YOU HAVE AWARENESS OF GLOBAL INEQUITY, WHICH WE DID NOT HAVE. AND WITH THAT AWARENESS, YOU LIKELY ALSO HAVE AN INFORMED CONSCIENCE THAT WILL TORMENT YOU IF YOU ABANDON THESE PEOPLE WHOSE LIVES YOU COULD CHANGE WITH VERY LITTLE EFFORT.

AND I HOPE YOU WILL COME BACK HERE TO HARVARD 30 YEARS FROM NOW AND REFLECT ON WHAT YOU HAVE DONE WITH YOUR TALENT AND YOUR ENERGY. I HOPE YOU WILL JUDGE YOURSELVES NOT ON YOUR PROFESSIONAL ACCOMPLISHMENTS ALONE, BUT ALSO ON HOW WELL YOU HAVE ADDRESSED THE WORLD'S DEEPEST INEQUITIES ... ON HOW WELL YOU TREATED PEOPLE A WORLD AWAY WHO HAVE NOTHING IN COMMON WITH YOU BUT THEIR HUMANITY. GOOD LUCK.

IN 2008 BILL GATES RETIRED FROM HIS DAY-TO-DAY WORK AT MICROSOFT.

"AFTER THE DEATH OF BILL GATES MOTHER, BILL PICKED UP WHERE SHE LEFT OFF WORKING WITH CHARITABLE ORGANIZATIONS, DONATING MONEY AND COMPUTERS TO UNDER PRIVILEGED SCHOOLS AND FAMILIES. WHILE HE WAS PUBLICLY AMASSING A FORTUNE, HE WAS ALSO QUIETLY GIVING AWAY A FORTUNE.

"IN 1994 WITH 94 MILLION DOLLARS BILL STARTED THE WILLIAM H. GATES FOUNDATION LATER TO BECOME THE BILL AND MELINDA GATES FOUNDATION.

"THEIR GOAL WAS NOTHING SHORT OF RIGHTING WHAT THEY SAW AS THE PROBLEMS OF THE WORLD. THE FOUNDATION WAS BUILT ON 15 GUIDING PRINCIPLES SET FOURTH BY THE GATES FAMILY, AND IT WOULD REACH OUT ALL OVER THE WORLD TO HELP PEOPLE BETTER THEMSELVES AND THEIR COMMUNITIES.

"WORKING WITH NATIONAL GOVERNMENTS AND UNICEF IN THE FIRST DECADE OF THE TWENTY-FIRST CENTURY, THE FOUNDATION SET OUT TO ERADICATE POLIO ONCE AND FOR ALL. I CAN TELL YOU PERSONALLY, THEIR EFFORTS WERE NOT IN VEIN."

BUT THE FOUNDATION ALSO HELPED OUT AT HOME IN THE US WITH GRANTS FOR EDUCATION AND WORKED TO MAKE SURE EVERYONE WAS GIVEN A FAIR SHOT NO MATTER WHERE THEY CAME FROM.

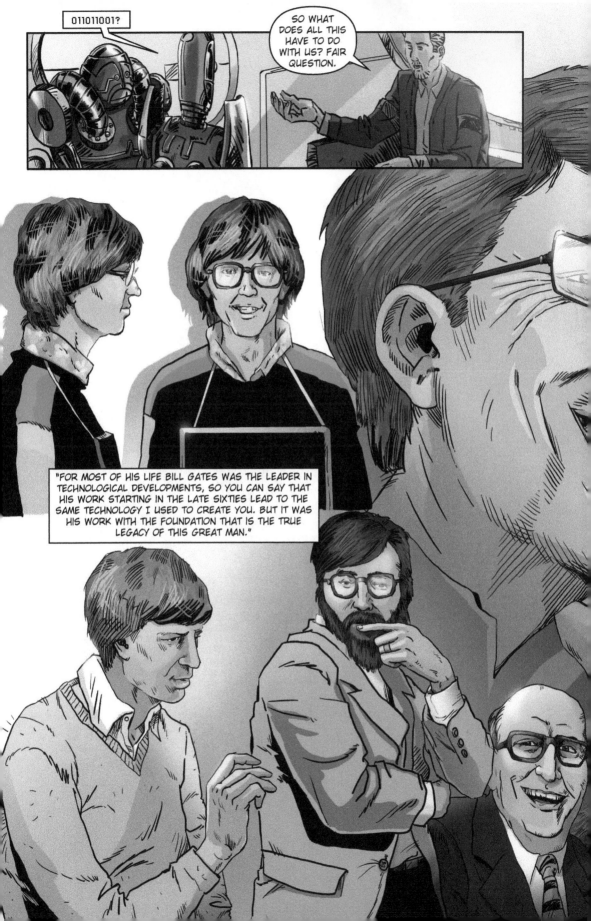

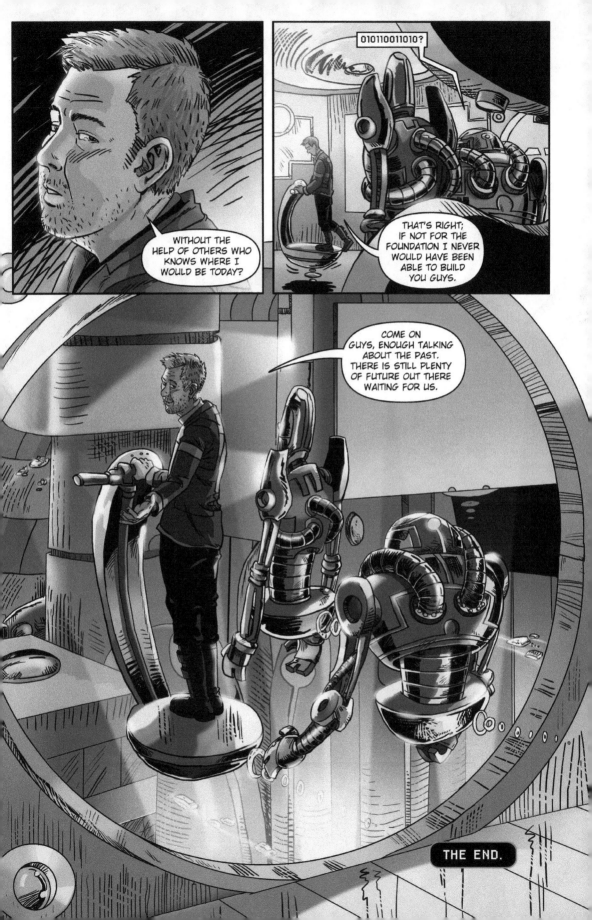

JACK DORSEY
TWITTER

ROCKETING ACROSS THE COUNTRY ON THIS AMTRAK TO ST. LOUIS....

THERE'S MORE TO THIS THAN YOU'RE *TELLING ME*. I CREATED TWITTER SO THAT PEOPLE COULD FIND NEW WAYS TO RECONNECT IN THE MODERN WORLD. AND IF YOU WON'T CONNECT WITH ME *HONESTLY*, THIS ENDS NOW.

ZOTT'S MEN...THINK I HAVE THE *CARL* CHIP.

DO YOU?

ONLY HALF. FATHER ENTRUSTED ME WITH IT, IN CASE... IN CASE.... OH, IT'S ALL OVER.

NOTHING'S OVER. WE STILL HAVE A CHANCE TO WIN.

WHAT DO YOU KNOW ABOUT HAVING THE ODDS AGAINST YOU?

I HELPED BUILD A PODCASTING COMPANY ONCE... *ODEO*. MY FRIENDS *EVAN WILLIAMS* AND *BIZ STONE* AND I PUT OUR ALL INTO IT ONLY TO HAVE *APPLE* SWOOP IN AND START PODCASTING WITH *ITUNES*. BUT DID WE GIVE UP?

NO! WE HAD INDEPENDENT PROJECTS. I CONCEIVED OF SENDING ONE TEXT THAT WOULD GO TO ALL OF MY FRIENDS. *NOAH GLASS*, HE WAS ODEO'S CO-FOUNDER; HE SHARED MY PASSION FOR THE PROJECT WE DUBBED, *"TWTTR."* WE RACKED UP THE BILLS TESTING IT OUT, BUT LOOK AT WHAT RESULTED. NOW WE JUST NEED TO SEE WHAT RESULTS IN...

ST. LOUIS!

IT SEEMS THE AUTHORITIES ARE AHEAD OF US.

COME OUT NOW, DORSEY, AND NO ONE GETS *HURT!*

THEY THINK YOU KIDNAPPED ME! IT'S ALL OVER MY TWITTER FEED!

NO TIME FOR THAT; WE GOTTA DASH! THIS IS MY OLD STOMPING GROUNDS! I KNOW A FEW HOMETOWN TRICKS THEY MIGHT NOT.

SECURITY PROTOCOL BLACK OMEGA!

DEATH TO INFERIOR INVADERS!

HIDE IN THE SHAFT, DOC!

IN THE WINK OF AN EYE, JACK DORSEY USES ANCIENT SECRETS TO SUMMON THE INNER CALM...

BEFORE THE STORM!

KillBot9000 chooses MERCY, Jack Dorsey.

THAT'S WHAT I CALL SUPERIOR!

DR. KANE, LET'S SHUT DOWN ZOTT'S OPERATION FOR GOOD.

UTTERLY IMPOSSIBLE. THIS IS THE POWER UNIT, BUT THE CONTROL MECHANISM IS A TAD...NORTH!

THE OBSERVATION DECK. SHE'S USING THE ENTIRE ARCH AS A MASSIVE *SATELLITE ANTENNA!*

CAN'T WE JUST PULL THE PLUG, DOCTOR?

NO, JACK. SHE CAN TAKE DOWN THE *WORLD*, MUCH LESS ENTIRE INTERNET. AND IF SHE GETS HER HANDS ON THE *CARL* CHIP, SHE WON'T EVEN NEED THE ARCH.

THEN LET'S *MOVE!*

KILLBOT 9000? WOULD YOU *CHOOSE* TO DO ME A FAVOR?

Such as?

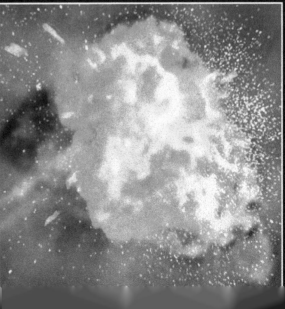

THE FUTURE!

ANY TIME YOU FIRE UP YOUR COMPUTER, I BET YOU SEE GOOGLE. IT'S EITHER THE FIRST PAGE YOU GO TO, OR THERE'S A SEARCH FUNCTION ON YOUR TOOLBAR. EITHER WAY, YOU KNOW *GOOGLE* AND YOU USE IT FREQUENTLY. YOU MIGHT HAVE EVEN USED IT RIGHT BEFORE READING THIS. BUT DO YOU KNOW THE MEN BEHIND THE PHENOMENA? DO YOU KNOW *SERGEY BRIN* AND *LARRY PAGE*?

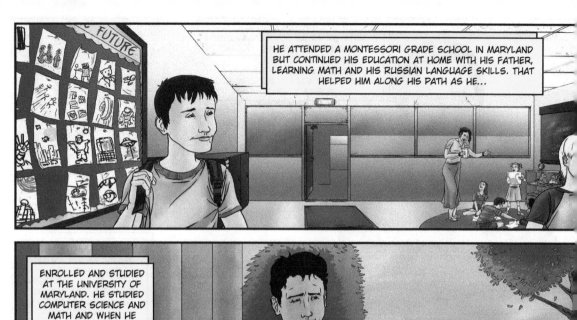

HE ATTENDED A MONTESSORI GRADE SCHOOL IN MARYLAND BUT CONTINUED HIS EDUCATION AT HOME WITH HIS FATHER, LEARNING MATH AND HIS RUSSIAN LANGUAGE SKILLS. THAT HELPED HIM ALONG HIS PATH AS HE...

ENROLLED AND STUDIED AT THE UNIVERSITY OF MARYLAND. HE STUDIED COMPUTER SCIENCE AND MATH AND WHEN HE GRADUATED IN 1993 WITH HONORS, JUST A FEW MONTHS SHORT OF HIS 20TH BIRTHDAY.

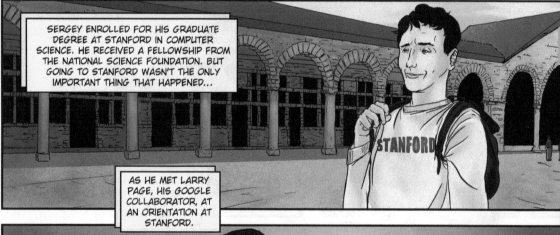

SERGEY ENROLLED FOR HIS GRADUATE DEGREE AT STANFORD IN COMPUTER SCIENCE. HE RECEIVED A FELLOWSHIP FROM THE NATIONAL SCIENCE FOUNDATION. BUT GOING TO STANFORD WASN'T THE ONLY IMPORTANT THING THAT HAPPENED...

AS HE MET LARRY PAGE, HIS GOOGLE COLLABORATOR, AT AN ORIENTATION AT STANFORD.

WE'RE BOTH KIND OF OBNOXIOUS.

BEFORE WE GET TO THE CREATION OF GOOGLE, THERE'S MORE TO BE SAID ABOUT SERGEY BEYOND JUST HIS FOUNDING OF GOOGLE. IN 2007, HE MARRIED ANNE WOJCICKI, A BIOTECH ANALYST AND YALE GRAD. THEY WERE MARRIED IN THE BAHAMAS...

AND BOTH SERGEY AND ANNE SHARE INTEREST IN HEALTH INFORMATION AND HAVE WORKED ALONGSIDE LEADING RESEARCHERS RELATED TO THE HUMAN GENOME PROJECT. THEY BOTH BELIEVE GENETICS ARE A DATABASE THAT CAN BE USED TO FIX PROBLEMS BEFORE THEY START, SIMILAR TO COMPUTER BUGS.

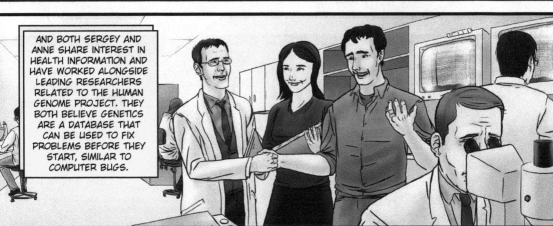

IN 2008, SERGEY'S MOTHER EUGENIA WAS DIAGNOSED WITH PARKINSON'S DISEASE AND INSTEAD OF HIDING BEHIND FEAR, HE MADE A LARGE DONATION TO THE UNIVERSITY OF MARYLAND SCHOOL OF MEDICINE WHERE HIS MOM WAS BEING TREATED AND ALSO LEARNED ABOUT HIS OWN GENETICS. HE LEARNED THAT HE AND HIS MOTHER BOTH POSSESS A MUTATION THAT MAKES THE LIKELIHOOD OF BEING DIAGNOSED WITH PARKINSON'S MUCH HIGHER.

HE DIDN'T HIDE OR COWER. HE FACED FORWARD AND ATTACKED THE POTENTIAL FOR THIS DISEASE WITH THE KNOWLEDGE THAT HE NOW HAD. ATTACKING A PROBLEM HEADFIRST IS SOMETHING SERGEY ALWAYS DOES, AND HE UNDERSTANDS THAT KNOWLEDGE IS THE MOST IMPORTANT STEP TOWARD PREVENTION.

HE HAS APPEARED ON A NUMBER OF TELEVISION PROGRAMS TO DISCUSS HIS BELIEFS AND HIS WORK WITH GOOGLE AND ELSEWHERE. HE'S BEEN ON CHARLIE ROSE, CNN, CNBC, AND MANY OTHERS.

HE'S AN INVESTOR IN TESLA MOTORS...

HE INVESTED $4.5 MILLION IN SPACE ADVEN-TURES, A SPACE TOURISM COMPANY THAT HAS SENT 7 PEOPLE INTO SPACE. HIS INVESTMENT ALSO ACTS AS HIS OWN CHANCE TO GET TO GO INTO SPACE IN THE NEAR FUTURE.

HE'S ALSO A MEMBER OF AmBAR, A GROUP WHOSE MEMBERS ARE ALL RUSSIAN-SPEAKING PROFESSIONALS. HE'S GIVEN MANY SPEECHES TO THESE GATHERED MEMBERS AT DIFFERENT EVENTS OVER TIME.

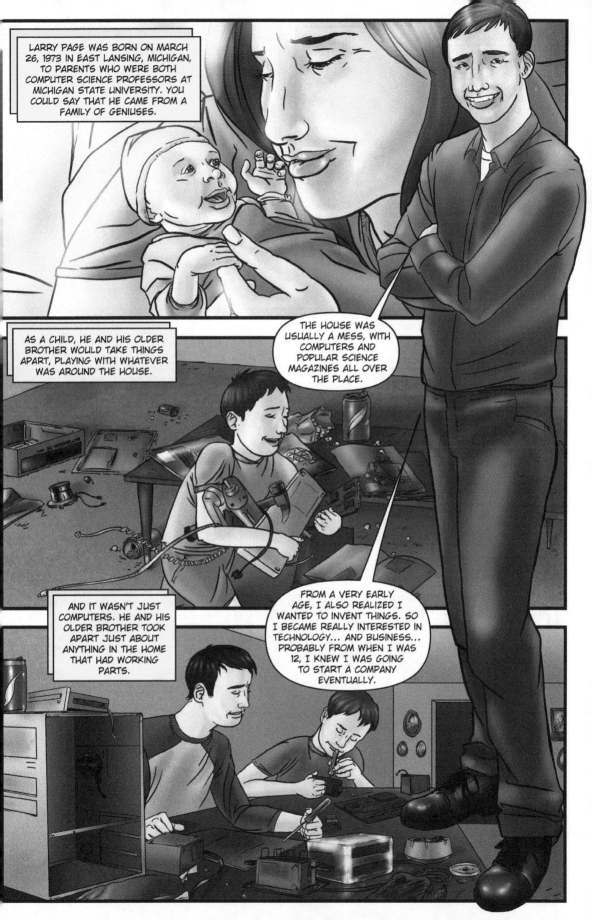

AFTER ATTENDING THE OKEMOS MONTESSORI SCHOOL IN MICHIGAN AND EAST LANSING HIGH SCHOOL, HE MOVED ONTO THE UNIVERSITY OF MICHIGAN.

HE RECEIVED A BACHELOR OF SCIENCE IN COMPUTER ENGINEERING AT THE UNIVERSITY OF MICHIGAN WITH HONORS.

HE WAS THE PRESIDENT OF THE ETA KAPPA NU FRATERNITY...

AS WELL AS A MEMBER OF THE MAIZE & BLUE SOLAR TEAM WHILE HE CONTINUED HIS STUDIES AT MICHIGAN.

ONCE HE FINISHED HIS DEGREE WITH HONORS AT THE UNIVERSITY OF MICHIGAN, HE ATTENDED STANFORD UNIVERSITY TO GET HIS MASTER'S DEGREE IN COMPUTER SCIENCE.

WHEN HE ENROLLED FOR HIS PH.D. PROGRAM AT STANFORD, HE MET SERGEY BRIN AT AN ORIENTATION FOR NEW STUDENTS. THE TWO WOULD SOON WORK WELL TOGETHER, BUT OUR STORY ON LARRY DOESN'T JUST STOP HERE.

HE QUICKLY BEGAN WORK ON HIS DISSERTATION BUT HAD TROUBLE, INITIALLY, WITH FINDING THE RIGHT PATH. HIS FIRST IDEA, WHICH WAS DISCUSSED AND ENCOURAGED BY HIS SUPERVISOR, WAS THE PROPERTIES OF THE WORLD WIDE WEB IN RELATION TO MATHEMATICS.

Address: http://www.findstuffandthings.com

HE BEGAN TO UNDERSTAND HOW WEB PAGES WERE CONNECTED, LOOKING AT HOW CERTAIN PAGES LINKED TOGETHER.

HE NICKNAMED THE PROJECT BACKRUB, WHICH WOULD EXPLAIN THAT THE INTERNET WAS ESSENTIALLY BASED ON CITATION. IT WAS A HUGE UNDERTAKING, AND IT BROUGHT THE ATTENTION OF SERGEY BRIN.

"THIS WAS THE MOST EXCITING PROJECT, BOTH BECAUSE IT TACKLED THE WEB, WHICH REPRESENTS HUMAN KNOWLEDGE, AND BECAUSE I LIKED LARRY."

IT WOULD BE THE BASIS FOR HOW GOOGLE BEGAN, BUT THIS ISN'T WHERE LARRY'S STORY ENDS.

IN 2007, HE MARRIED LUCINDA SOUTHWORTH, A RESEARCH SCIENTIST. THE TWO WERE MARRIED IN THE CARIBBEAN AND HAVE SINCE HAD A CHILD TOGETHER.

JUST LIKE SERGEY, HE IS ALSO AN INVESTOR IN THE TESLA MOTOR COMPANY, THE CREATORS OF THE TESLA ROADSTER.

LARRY AND SERGEY HAVE ALSO ACTED AS FILM PRODUCERS, ON SUCH FILMS AS BROKEN ARROWS. IT IS JUST ONE OF MANY OF THEIR EXCITING BUSINESS VENTURES TOGETHER OR APART.

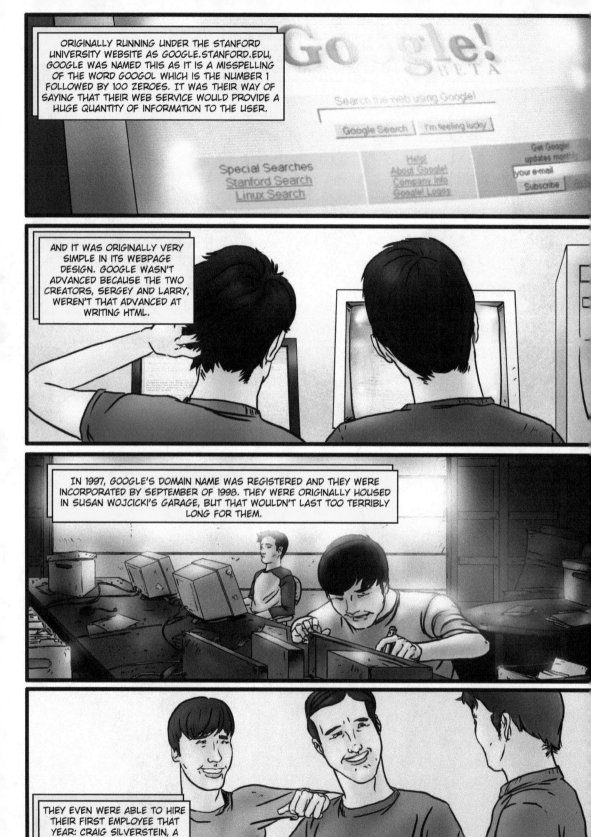

ORIGINALLY RUNNING UNDER THE STANFORD UNIVERSITY WEBSITE AS GOOGLE.STANFORD.EDU, GOOGLE WAS NAMED THIS AS IT IS A MISSPELLING OF THE WORD GOOGOL WHICH IS THE NUMBER 1 FOLLOWED BY 100 ZEROES. IT WAS THEIR WAY OF SAYING THAT THEIR WEB SERVICE WOULD PROVIDE A HUGE QUANTITY OF INFORMATION TO THE USER.

AND IT WAS ORIGINALLY VERY SIMPLE IN ITS WEBPAGE DESIGN. GOOGLE WASN'T ADVANCED BECAUSE THE TWO CREATORS, SERGEY AND LARRY, WEREN'T THAT ADVANCED AT WRITING HTML.

IN 1997, GOOGLE'S DOMAIN NAME WAS REGISTERED AND THEY WERE INCORPORATED BY SEPTEMBER OF 1998. THEY WERE ORIGINALLY HOUSED IN SUSAN WOJCICKI'S GARAGE, BUT THAT WOULDN'T LAST TOO TERRIBLY LONG FOR THEM.

THEY EVEN WERE ABLE TO HIRE THEIR FIRST EMPLOYEE THAT YEAR: CRAIG SILVERSTEIN, A FELLOW PHD STUDENT. IT WOULD BE SOME OF THEIR FIRST MOVES ON THE ROAD TO WHERE THEY ARE TODAY, BUT FAR FROM THEIR LAST.

PRETTY EARLY ON, THEY RECEIVED $100,000 OF FUNDING FROM THE CO-FOUNDER OF SUN MICROSYSTEMS EVEN BEFORE THEY WERE INCORPORATED. BUT SERGEY AND LARRY ALSO DECIDED, WHILE THEY WERE STILL STUDENTS IN 1999, THAT GOOGLE WAS TAKING UP TOO MUCH OF THEIR TIME. THEY HAD NO TIME TO STUDY AND NO TIME FOR PRETTY MUCH ANYTHING ELSE, SO THEY BEGAN TO TAKE MEETINGS WITH BUSINESSMEN SUCH AS EXCITE CEO GEORGE BELL, OFFERING TO SELL HIM THE COMPANY FOR $1 MILLION. THANKFULLY FOR SERGEY AND LARRY, THE CEO DECLINED THE OFFER.

THEY DID END UP OBTAINING FUNDING, WITH UP TO $25 MILLION COMING MAINLY FROM VENTURE CAPITAL FIRMS LIKE SEQUOIA CAPITAL AND KLEINER PERKINS CAULFIELD AND BYERS.

ONCE FUNDING STARTED TO RISE, THEY WERE ABLE TO MOVE FROM THEIR HUMBLE GARAGE BEGINNINGS TO A MORE SUITABLE PLACE OF BUSINESS, MOVING INTO AN OFFICE IN PALO ALTO, CALIFORNIA. THEY WOULDN'T LAST LONG IN THESE OFFICES, AS GOOGLE CONTINUED TO GROW.

AS GOOGLE GREW, DESPITE THEIR BEST INTENTIONS, SO DID THE NEED FOR ADVERTISEMENTS. THE ADS WERE SOLD BASED ON KEYWORDS IN A SEARCH AND WOULD BE TEXT-BASED ONLY.

Sponsored Links

Sasquatch Feeder
Find Bird Feeders, squirrel za
and more at www.feedersforf
http://www.feedersforfuzzyfriends.com

Squirrel Zapper
Find Bird Feeders, squirrel za
and more at www.feedersforf
http://www.feedersforfuzzyfriends.com

Edible Sandals

AMONG OTHER MAJOR EVENTS IN THE FIRST COUPLE YEARS OF THE DEVELOPMENT AND GROWTH OF GOOGLE, THEY WERE GRANTED A PATENT ON THE PAGERANK MECHANISM, LISTING LARRY PAGE AS THE INVENTOR AND ASSIGNED TO STANFORD UNIVERSITY. IT WAS ANOTHER IN A LONG LIST OF THINGS THAT HELPED TO LEGITIMIZE THE SMALL BUT BLOSSOMING COMPANY.

GOOGLE HAS BEEN NAMED THE MOST DESIRABLE AND MOST ATTRACTIVE EMPLOYER TO GRADUATING STUDENTS ACROSS THE COUNTRY. OBVIOUSLY, MOST PEOPLE CAN SEE THAT THEIR INFORMALITIES AND THEIR WORK ETHIC ARE THE REASONS FOR THIS.

SOME OF THE PRINCIPLES OF GOOGLE INCLUDE: YOU CAN BE SERIOUS WITHOUT A SUIT...

WORK SHOULD BE CHALLENGING AND THE CHALLENGE SHOULD BE FUN...

AND YOU CAN MAKE MONEY WITHOUT BEING EVIL.

AND GOOGLE'S INVENTORS AND CHAIRMAN, SERGEY, LARRY AND ERIC, RESPECTIVELY, DO THEIR BEST TO FOLLOW ALL OF THESE PRINCIPLES. AFTER GOOGLE'S INITIAL PUBLIC OFFERING, THE PERFORMANCE OF THEIR STOCK WENT THROUGH THE ROOF, ALLOWING THEM TO BE COMPENSATED QUITE HIGHLY BY THEIR STOCKS. BECAUSE OF THIS, THEY ALL REQUESTED THAT THEIR SALARIES BE CUT TO $1, AND EVERY TIME THE QUESTION OF A RAISE OR AN INCREASE IN SALARY HAS BEEN BROUGHT UP, ALL THREE HAVE TURNED IT DOWN.

IN THEIR QUEST TO NEVER DO EVIL, GOOGLE SUPPORTS NET NEUTRALITY. THEY EVEN HAVE A GUIDE TO IT, WHICH SAYS:

NET NEUTRALITY IS ABOUT EQUAL ACCESS TO THE INTERNET. IN OUR VIEW, THE BROADBAND CARRIERS SHOULD NOT BE PERMITTED TO USE THEIR MARKET POWER TO DISCRIMINATE AGAINST COMPETING APPLICATIONS OR CONTENT. JUST AS TELEPHONE COMPANIES ARE NOT PERMITTED TO TELL CONSUMERS WHO THEY CAN CALL OR WHAT THEY CAN SAY, BROADBAND CARRIERS SHOULD NOT BE ALLOWED TO USE THEIR MARKET POWER TO CONTROL ACTIVITY ONLINE.

Mr. Cerf

AND IN 2006, VINCENT CERF, A CO-INVENTOR OF INTERNET PROTOCOL AND THE CHIEF INTERNET EVANGELIST AND VICE PRESIDENT OF GOOGLE, TESTIFIED BEFORE CONGRESS ABOUT NET NEUTRALITY.

ALLOWING BROADBAND CARRIERS TO CONTROL WHAT PEOPLE SEE AND DO ONLINE WOULD FUNDAMENTALLY UNDERMINE THE PRINCIPLES THAT HAVE MADE THE INTERNET SUCH A SUCCESS.

CONTINUING THEIR PLANS TO SAVE THE WORLD BY ANY MEANS THAT THEY CAN, GOOGLE FORMED GOOGLE.ORG, A NOT-FOR-PROFIT ORGANIZATION THAT THEY GAVE $1 BILLION AS A START-UP FUND.

ONE OF THEIR FIRST PROJECTS WAS AN ELECTRIC HYBRID CAR THAT WOULD GET 100 MILES PER GALLON AND THEIR FIRST EXECUTIVE DIRECTOR WAS DR. LARRY BRILLIANT. THEIR MISSION, WHICH IS STILL ONGOING UNDER CURRENT DIRECTOR MEGAN SMITH, IS TO CREATE AWARENESS ON GLOBAL PUBLIC HEALTH, CLIMATE CHANGE, AND GLOBAL POVERTY.

GOOGLE HAS EVEN EMPLOYED IDEAS THAT SOME MIGHT FIND A BIT CONFUS-ING OR ODD IN ORDER TO LOWER THEIR CARBON FOOTPRINT. THEY ANNOUNCED PLANS IN 2006 TO INSTALL SOLAR PANELS ON THEIR BUILDINGS IN ORDER TO PROVIDE 30% OF THEIR ENERGY NEEDS ON CAMPUS. WHILE THAT WAS NEITHER CONFUSING NOR ODD, THEY DID ALSO EMPLOY THE USE OF HERDS OF GOATS TO KEEP THE GRASS AROUND THE CAMPUS SHORT. THIS WAS USED TO CUT BACK ON THE USE OF MOWERS AND THEIR GAS USAGE AS WELL AS TO KEEP THE GRASS SHORT TO CUT BACK ON THE POSSIBILITY OF BUSH FIRES.

IN SPITE OF THEIR WORK TO HELP SAVE THE ENVIRONMENT OR CUT BACK ON THEIR OWN CARBON FOOTPRINT, GOOGLE WAS ACCUSED OF BEING AN ENERGY GLUTTON AND OF USING THESE VERY PUBLIC CAMPAIGNS AS A WAY TO COVER UP THEIR MASSIVE ENERGY USAGE.

Google: Energy Gluttons
by Johnny Expectorant

Space Tea
by Irena M.

TO GO ALONG WITH THE CORPORATE CULTURE OF HAVING FUN AND ENJOYING WHAT YOU DO, OVER THE YEARS, GOOGLE HAS EMPLOYED BOTH EASTER EGGS AND APRIL FOOL'S JOKES AS PART OF ITS ONGOING CORPORATE IDENTITY. YOU CAN MAKE THE GOOGLE HOMEPAGE DO A BARREL ROLL, WE'VE SEEN THE HOMEPAGE'S NAME CHANGED TO TOPEKA IN ORDER OF THE NEW GOOGLE FIBER PROJECT, YOU CAN USE YOUR BODY TO SEND EMAILS (BUT ONLY ON APRIL 1ST THROUGH GMAIL MOTION), AND YOU CAN EVEN GET THE ANSWER TO THE ULTIMATE QUESTION OF LIFE, THE UNIVERSE AND EVERYTHING. AND THAT ANSWER IS 42.

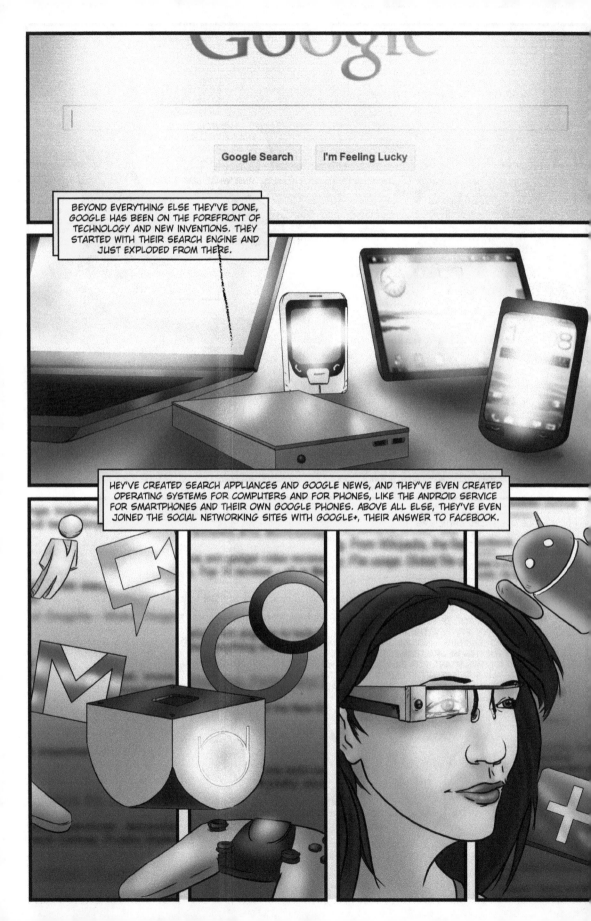

AND NO MATTER WHAT THE TWO MEN DO, THE WORLD WILL STOP AND TAKE NOTICE. AS THE INVENTORS OF GOOGLE, THEY HAVE GIVEN THE WORLD SOMETHING THAT MAKES ALL INTERNET SEARCHES EASIER AND MORE ENJOYABLE, WHERE KNOWLEDGE IS JUST A CLICK AWAY. AND AS THINGS CHANGE AND THE WORLD CHANGES AROUND THEM, LARRY PAGE AND SERGEY BRIN HAVE PROVEN THAT THEY ARE NOT GOING TO SIT IDLY BY AND LET THE WORLD CHANGE AROUND THEM. THEY ARE GOING TO CONTINUE TO INNOVATE AND CHANGE WITH THE WORLD, AND GOOGLE WILL ALWAYS BE ON THE FOREFRONT OF THAT CHANGE.

THE END

A gun was waved in Mark's face and then just as quickly and inexplicably as Mark's assailant had appeared, he disappeared into the shadows.

Reflecting on the incident afterward, Mark would say he was very lucky that his life was not cut short that evening and that he was able to accomplish all he has since.

Which has included Facebook Beacon, a new social advertising system that would enable people to share information with Facebook friends based on their browsing activities on other sites. An eBay seller, for instance, could let friends know automatically what they have for sale via Facebook's news feed as they list items.

Mark announced Facebook Beacon on November 6, 2007 in Los Angeles. The program came under heavy criticism from both civil liberties groups and individual users, who cited privacy concerns.

Since his brush with death, Mark has also been featured on "60 Minutes" and been named one of "The World's Most Influential People " by "Time" Magazine.

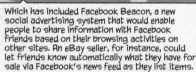

He has also been able to grow his company at an astonishingly prodigious pace, to the point where he was able to reject an offer from Google in 2007 for a stake in the company.

In October of that year, he decided to go instead with Microsoft, selling a 1.6% stake for $240 million.

This means that Facebook had a market value of $15 billion at the time of the sale

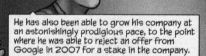

Though Mark failed to respond to the concerns at first, he ultimately wrote a blog post on Facebook taking responsibility for issues with Beacon and offering an easier way for users to opt out of the service.

As of December, 2009 Facebook claimed that it had attained over 350 million users and it has been estimated that Mark himself is currently worth at least $3 billion.

The astonishing luck that enabled him to survive the incident at the gas station and that has played a part in his achievements before and since, has combined with his incredible intelligence and ambition to make Mark not only an extremely wealthy man, but one of the most powerful and influential people in the world.

Despite what anyone says about him, pro and con, it all boils down to a quote he has imprinted on his business card.

What is the quote on the card? You'll find out later. First, let's see how someone who has had and continues to have a profound effect on our society got to this point.

Mark Elliot Zuckerberg was born on May 14, 1984 in White Plains, New York and eventually raised in Dobbs Ferry, New York.

Mark was an extremely bright child and it was evident early on that he enjoyed developing computer programs, especially communication tools and games.

Mark went to school at Ardsley High School before attending Phillips Exeter Academy.

While attending Phillips Exeter Academy, he built a program to help the workers in his father's office communicate.

Around the same time, he built a version of the game Risk and a music player named Synapse that used artificial intelligence to learn the user's listening habits.

Synapse generated a lot of buzz and impressed a lot of people, including Bill Gates - who obviously knows intelligent innovation when he sees it.

Microsoft was among those that tried to purchase Synapse and recruit Mark, reportedly offering him between one and two million dollars to go work for them.

Amazingly, 17-year old Mark turned them down. Like Gates himself as a young man, Mark had bigger dreams and goals, starting with deciding to attend Harvard University.

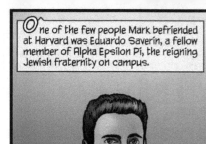

One of the few people Mark befriended at Harvard was Eduardo Saverin, a fellow member of Alpha Epsilon Pi, the reigning Jewish fraternity on campus.

Epsilon Pi was for more secular kids, the one whose last name was their most recognizable Jewish feature.

To Epsilon Pi kids, a Jewish girlfriend might be nice because it would make their mom and dad happy. But, in reality, an Asian girlfriend was more likely.

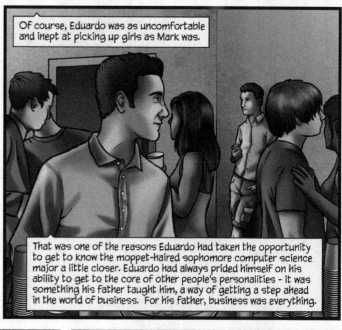

Of course, Eduardo was as uncomfortable and inept at picking up girls as Mark was.

That was one of the reasons Eduardo had taken the opportunity to get to know the moppet-haired sophomore computer science major a little closer. Eduardo had always prided himself on his ability to get to the core of other people's personalities - it was something his father taught him, a way of getting a step ahead in the world of business. For his father, business was everything.

The son of wealthy immigrants who had barely escaped the Holocaust to Brazil during World War II, his father had raised Eduardo in the sometimes harsh light of survivors.

BRAZIL

He came from a long line of businessmen who knew how important it was to succeed - whatever one's circumstances.

FLORIDA

Brazil was only the beginning. The Saverin family had almost just as hastily been forced to relocate to Miami when Eduardo was thirteen - when it was discovered that Eduardo's name had ended up on a kidnap list because of his father's financial success.

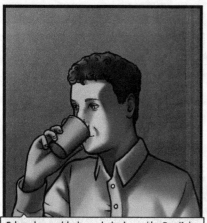

Eduardo would struggle to learn the English language and Miami culture in junior high. As a result, even though he knew nothing about computers, he completely understood what it was like being the awkward outsider and different, regardless of the reason.

THIS IS FUN.

YEAH. AT LEAST THE PUNCH HAS RUM IN IT THIS YEAR. LAST TIME, I THINK IT WAS CAPRI SUN. THEY WENT ALL OUT THIS TIME AROUND.

Eduardo felt that Mark stood out, and not just because he was a bit on the gawky side - like Eduardo himself - or because he was wearing cargo shorts instead of slacks and sandals with no socks.

No, even in a fraternity made up entirely of Jewish kids, many of them geeky kids who made algorithms out of fetishes and had nothing better to do on a Friday night than hang out in a classroom filled with crepe paper and colored posters, talking about girls they weren't actually getting, Mark stood out by appearing to be incredibly smart possibly a true genius.

Eduardo decided, for all his social awkwardness, Mark would be a good person to become friends with. Anyone who'd turned down a million dollars from Bill Gates at 17 almost certainly was going somewhere.

So Eduardo had reasons he could relate to and respect Mark.

I HAVE A FEELING THIS IS GONNA BREAK UP IN A FEW MINUTES. I'M HEADING BACK TO THE RIVER - ELIOT HOUSE. WHAT HOUSE ARE YOU IN AGAIN?

KIRKLAND.

He had no doubt Mark was a genius after he'd followed up Synapse with a program he'd written at Harvard called Course Match that allowed kids to see what classes other kids had signed up for.

Eduardo had checked out Course Match once or twice, trying to track down random hot girls he'd met in the dining hall, to no avail.

But the program was good enough to get a pretty big following. Most of the campus appreciated Course Match - if not the kid who created it.

IF YOU WANT, THERE'S A PARTY ON MY FLOOR WE COULD CHECK OUT. IT'S GONNA SUCK, BUT CERTAINLY NO WORSE THAN THIS.

WHY NOT? I'VE GOT A PROBLEM SET DUE TOMORROW, BUT I'M BETTER AT LOGARITHMS DRUNK THAN SOBER.

But Eduardo did and wanted to get to know the computer genius.

It was a old Harvard tradition. Kids attempting to have sex on the automatic, vast bookshelves on the wheeled tracks - that few had actually achieved.

SENIOR YEAR, I'M GOING TO HAVE SEX IN THOSE STACKS. I SWEAR, IT'S GONNA HAPPEN.

BABY STEPS. MAYBE YOU SHOULD TRY GETTING A GIRL TO YOUR DORM FIRST.

THINGS AREN'T THAT BAD. I'M PUNCHING THE PHOENIX.

CONGRATULATIONS.

The Phoenix was one of the eight all-male clubs that had nurtured generations of world leaders and power brokers.

The Porcellian was the oldest club, whose past members had names like Roosevelt and Rockefeller. The Fly Club was considered the preppiest club and had spawned two presidents and a handful of billionaires.

The Phoenix was the social king of the hill and admission meant that not only were you part of an exclusive, century-old network, but you also got to spend your weekends surrounded by the hottest girls culled from schools all over the 02138.

WELL, IF I GET IN, MAYBE I CAN PUT YOUR NAME ON THE LIST. FOR NEXT YEAR. YOU CAN PUNCH AS A JUNIOR.

THAT WOULD BE - INTERESTING.

IF YOU GET TO KNOW SOME OF THE OTHER MEMBERS, YOU'LL HAVE A GOOD SHOT. I'M SURE A LOT OF THEM USED YOUR COURSE MATCH PROGRAM.

Of course, Eduardo knew as soon as he said it that Phoenix members weren't going to get excited by Mark because of some computer program. A computer program couldn't get you laid. You got popular - and sometimes laid - by going to parties and hanging out with pretty girls.

One look at Mark and it was obvious to Eduardo that his new friend didn't know the first thing about the sort of social networking one had to master to get into a club like the Phoenix.

Certainly, he had no way of knowing that one day soon Mark was going to take the entire concept of a social network and turn it on it's head. That one day this awkward kid with the curly hair was going to change Eduardo's life more than the Phoenix ever could.

Eduardo felt that in a few short weeks, he and Mark had become close friends. He felt they had a similar spirit and had begun to think of him like a real brother, not just someone who shared a Jewish frat and was pretty sure Mark felt the same way about him.

So sure that he could share an uncomfortable but amusing secret with him.

OH, SHIT.

YEAH.

THAT'S NOT –

YES, IT IS.

It was the kind of moment true friends remember forever. As part of Eduardo's Phoenix initiation he had been instructed to keep a chicken with him at all times, to carry it with him everywhere, day and night, to every class, dining hall and dorm room he visited. He even had to sleep with it. For five whole days, his only job had been to keep that chicken alive.

THAT'S GREAT. I REALLY LIKE YOUR NEW FRIEND. HE'S A MUCH BETTER CONVERSATIONALIST THAN YOU ARE.

IT'S NOT GREAT! THIS CHICKEN IS A PAIN IN THE ASS. AND IT'S CAUSED ME A WHOLE SHITLOAD OF TROUBLE.

I'VE GOT TO GET OUT OF HERE BEFORE THIS THING ERUPTS AGAIN! BUT I JUST WANTED TO MAKE SURE WE'RE STILL ON FOR TONIGHT.

WHAT'S HER NAME AGAIN? THE FRIEND, I MEAN?

MONICA.

AND SHE'S HOT?

Eduardo had met a cute, slim Asian girl named Angie at a Phoenix event. Eduardo had convinced her to bring a friend along so the four of them could meet up for a drink.

The truth was, Eduardo had no idea if Monica was hot or not. He'd never seen the girl. But in his mind, neither one of them had the right to be so choosy.

Up until now, the ladies hadn't exactly been knocking down doors to get to them.

Now that Eduardo was almost in the Phoenix, he was starting to have access to women and he was determined to bring his friend along with him. He couldn't yet get Mark into the Phoenix himself – but he could certainly introduce him to a girl or two.

As Eduardo left the classroom in his shirt and tie, he had two simple requests of Mark.

JUST BE THERE AT EIGHT. AND MARK?

YEAH?

WEAR SOMETHING NICE FOR A CHANGE.

Behind every great fortune, there lies a great crime.

If Balzac had somehow risen from the dead to witness Mark Zuckerberg storm into his Kirkland dorm that monumental evening during the last week of October 2003, he might have amended his famous words.

Because that historical moment, one that inarguably led to one of the greatest fortunes in modern history, did not begin so much with a crime, but a college prank.

If the newly revived Balzac had been there in that spartan, claustrophobic dorm, he might have seen Mark head straight for his computer.

There would have been no question that the kid was angry and that he was probably wearing his Adidas flip flops and one day he was determined to be in a position where those were the only shoes he'd ever have to wear.

Mark took a deep swig of the beer, let the bitter taste at the back of his throat, as he tapped his fingers on the laptop keyboard, gently summoning the thing awake.

Since high school, it could be observed, his thoughts had always seemed clearer when he let them come out through his hands. To an outside observer, the relationship he had with his computer seemed much smoother than any relationship he'd ever had with anyone in the outside world.

Mark never seemed happier than when he was looking at a computer screen. Maybe, deep down, it had something to do with control.

It was almost a symbiosis that had grown after years and years of practice. When Mark's fingers touched his keyboard, it felt like the only place he belonged.

By a little after eight that evening, Mark opened up a fresh blog page and unleashed an idea that had been percolating in his mind for days.

The frustration over the evening he just had was simply the impetus for him to move forward with an idea - starting with a title.

Harvard Face mash/The Process

8:13 PM: ***** is a bitch. I need to think of something to make to take my mind off her. I need to think of something to occupy my mind. Easy enough now i just need an idea.

He might have looked at the words for a few minutes, wondering if he was really going to go through with this. He might have taken another drink from his beer and hunched forward over his keys.

Maybe somewhere inside of Mark's thoughts, he knew that blaming it all on a girl who had rejected him wasn't exactly fair. How were this one girl's actions different from the way most girls had treated Mark throughout high school and college?

Even Eduardo, geek that he was, had better luck with girls than Mark Zuckerberg did. And now that Eduardo was getting into the Phoenix, well, tonight Mark was going to do something about his situation.

He was going to create something that would give him back some of that control, show all of them what he could do.

Perhaps he took another drink, then turned his attention toward the desktop computer next to his laptop. He hit a few keys and the desktop's screen whirred to life.

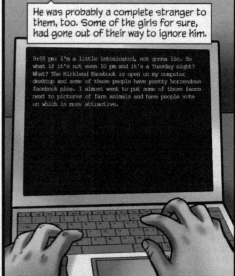

He quickly opened up his Internet connection, linking himself to the school's network. A few more clicks of the keys and he was ready.

He turned back to his laptop, went back to work on his big idea and grinned as he scanned through the pictures that were now spread across the screen of his desktop.

Certainly, he recognized some of the guys, and even a few of the girls - but most of them were probably strangers to him, even if he'd passed them in the dining hall or on his way to his classes.

He was probably a complete stranger to them, too. Some of the girls for sure, had gone out of their way to ignore him.

9:48 pm: I'm a little intoxicated, not gonna lie. So what if it's not even 10 pm and it's a Tuesday night? What? The Kirkland Facebook is open on my computer desktop and some of these people have pretty horrendous facebook pics. I almost want to put some of these faces next to pictures of farm animals and have people vote on which is more attractive.

At some point during this process, Mark began to exchange ideas with his friends who had gotten home from dinner, classes, drinks - most of the communication coming, as it usually did, via e-mail.

Nobody in his inner circle used the phone much anymore; it was all e-mail. Other than Eduardo, they were all almost as infatuated with their computers as Mark was.

Mark turned back to the blog.

It's not such a great idea and probably not even funny, but Billy comes up with the idea of comparing two people from thefacebook, and only sometimes putting a farm animal in there. Good call, Mr. Olson! I think he's onto something.

Yes, to a kid like Mark it must have indeed seemed a great idea. The Kirkland housing facebook - all of the school's facebooks, as their databases of student photos were known - was such a stagnant thing, compiled entirely in alphabetical order by the university.

The percolations that must have gripped Mark's imagination for a few days were now forming into something real - an idea for a Web site.

To Mark, it's likely that the cool thing was the math that was going into it: the computer science of the task, the code at the heart of the Web site idea. There was some complexity to it that his friends would surely appreciate - even if the larger campus of bimbos and neanderthals never understood.

11:09pm: Yea, it's on. I'm not exactly sure how the farm animals are going to fit into this whole thing (you can't really ever be sure with farm animals) but I like the idea of comparing two people together. It gives the whole thing a very Turing feel, since people's ratings of the pictures will be more implicit than, say, choosing a number to represent each person's hotness like they do on hotornot.com.

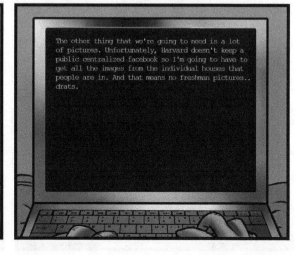

The other thing that we're going to need is a lot of pictures. Unfortunately, Harvard doesn't keep a public centralized facebook so I'm going to have to get all the images from the individual houses that people are in. And that means no freshman pictures.. drats.

By this point, Mark likely knew he was about to cross a line - but then, he'd never been very god at staying within the lines. That was Eduardo's game, wearing a jacket and tie, joining the Phoenix, playing along with everyone else in the sandbox. From Mark's history, it was obvious he didn't like the sandbox. He seemed the type who wanted to kick out all the sand.

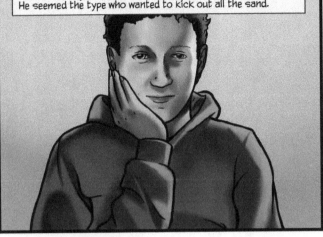

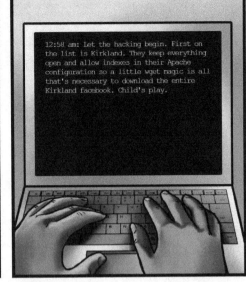

12:58 am: Let the hacking begin. First on the list is Kirkland. They keep everything open and allow indexes in their Apache configuration so a little wget magic is all that's necessary to download the entire Kirkland facebook. Child's play.

It really was that simple - for Mark. Most likely, in a matter of minutes, he had all the pictures from the Kirkland facebook downloaded off of the university's servers and into his laptop. Sure, in a sense it was stealing - he didn't have the legal right to those pictures, and the university certainly didn't put them up there for someone to download them. But then, if information was getable, didn't Mark have the right to get it? What sort of evil authority could decide that he wasn't allowed access to something he so easily could access?

1:03 am: Next on the list is Eliot. They're also open, but with no indexes in Apache. I can run an empty search and it returns all of the images in the database in a single page. Then I can save the page and Mozilla will save all the mages for me. Excellent. Moving right along...

Mark was now deep in a hacker's paradise. Breaking into Harvard's computer system was really child's play to him. He was smarter than anyone Harvard had employed to make the system, he was smarter than the administration, and he was certainly smarter than the security systems Harvard had put in place.

Really, he was teaching them a lesson - showing them the flaws in their system. He was doing a good deed, though it was pretty likely that they wouldn't have seen it that way. But hey, Mark was documenting what he was doing right there in his blog. And when he built the website, he was going to put that blog right there on the site for everyone to see. Maybe a little crazy, but that was going to be the icing on the cake.

1:06 am: Lowell has some security. Suspicions affirmed - time to get myself a matching name and student ID combo for Lowell and I'm in. But there are more problems. The pictures are separated into a bunch of different pages and I'm way too lazy to go through all of them and save each one. Writing a perl script to take care of that seems like the right answer. Indeed.

It was hacking at it's most fundamental. By now, Mark's computer was filling up with pictures; pretty soon he'd have half the house photo database in his hands. Every girl on campus - except the freshmen - under his control; in his laptop, little electronic bytes and bits that represented all those pretty and not so pretty faces, blondes and brunettes and redheads, big-breasted and small, tall and short. All of them. Every girl. This was going to be fantastic.

1:31 am: Adams has no security, but limits the number results to 20 a page. All I need to do is break out the same script I just used on Lowell and we're set.

House by house, name by alphabetical name, he was collecting them all.

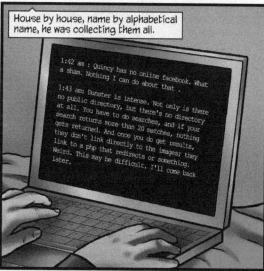

1:42 am : Quincy has no online facebook. What a sham. Nothing I can do about that .

1:43 am: Dunster is intense. Not only is there no public directory, but there's no directory at all. You have to do searches, and if your search returns more than 20 matches, nothing gets returned. And once you do get results, they don't link directly to the images; they link to a php that redirects or something. Weird. This may be difficult. I'll come back later.

The houses he couldn't get through right away, he'd most likely figure out later. There was no wall he couldn't climb. Harvard was the premier university in the world, but it was no match for Mark Zuckerberg and his computer.

1:52 am: Leverett is a little better. They still make you search, but you can do an empty search and get links to pages with ever student's picture. It's slightly obnoxious that they only let you view one picture at a time and there's no way i'm going to go to 500 pages to download pics one at a time so it's definitely necessary to break out emacs and modify that perl script. This time it's going to look at the directory and figure out what what pages it needs to go to by finding links with regexes. Then it'll just go to all of the pages it found links to and jack the images from them. It's taking a few tries to compile the script...another Beck's is in order.

Mark was most likely wide-awake now, deep into the process. He didn't care what time it was, or how late it got. To guys like Mark, time was another weapon of the establishment, like alphabetical order. The great engineers, hackers - they didn't function under the same time constraints as everyone else.

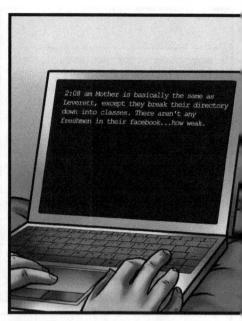

2:08 am Mother is basically the same as Leverett, except they break their directory down into classes. There aren't any freshmen in their facebook...how weak.

And on and on he went, into the night. By 4AM, it seemed as though he had gone as far as he could go - downloaded thousands of photos from the houses' databases. It was likely that there were a few houses that weren't accessible online from his James Bond-like lair in Kirkland House - you probably needed an IP address from within these houses to get at them. But it was also likely that Mark knew how to do that - it would just take a little legwork. In a few days, he would have everything he needed.

Mark grinned as he downed his Beck's, realizing that once he had all the data, he'd just have to write the algorithms. Complex mathematical programs to make the Web sire work. Then the program itself. It would take a day, maybe two at the most.

He was going to call the site Facemash.com. And it was going to be beautiful.

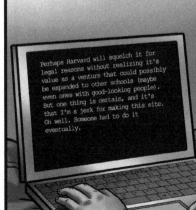

Perhaps Harvard will squelch it for legal reasons without realizing it's value as a venture that could possibly be expanded to other schools (maybe even ones with good-looking people). But one thing is certain, and it's that I'm a jerk for making this site. Oh well. Someone had to do it eventually.

Were we let in for our looks? No. Will we be judged on them? Yes.

Mark looked at his 15-word introduction and all he had done in one night and was very impressed with it.

THIS IS GOING TO BE FUCKING BEAUTIFUL!

Despite all his skill, there were certain Harvard residence houses Mark was having a hard time hacking into.

He was determined to remedy the situation. He wanted to prove what he could do.

Prove how much smarter he was from everybody else.

The places where Mark wanted to get to weren't exactly off limits, but you needed a key to get inside.

Without a key, he simply had to time things perfectly, lunging inside, leaving a textbook levered in the door frame.

Mark's plan was almost foiled by a guy and girl who figured fortune had smiled upon them by having someone leave the door to a normally off-limits room ajar - and came close to using it to get lucky.

Fortunately, for Mark, the girl changed her mind.

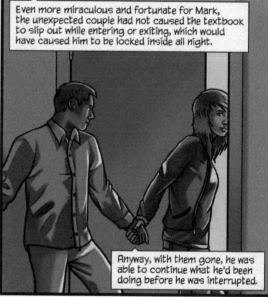

Even more miraculous and fortunate for Mark, the unexpected couple had not caused the textbook to slip out while entering or exiting, which would have caused him to be locked inside all night.

Anyway, with them gone, he was able to continue what he'd been doing before he was interrupted.

Mark couldn't wait to have his fingers on his computer's keyboard again, to cull as much pure energy as he could from the building itself.

As Mark's laptop continued to suck up as much electrical information as it could, Mark's heart started pounding.

As the seconds continued ticking by, Mark kept glancing behind himself to see if the room was still empty.

He knows what he is doing is probably illegal and definitely against school rules.

This wasn't the first time Mark had done something like this and the adrenaline high was always the same.

He felt like James Bond. Despite, as far as hacking goes, he didn't even consider what he was doing to be equal to shoplifting.

Mark justified his actions by telling himself he wasn't stealing money from a bank or hacking into a Defense Department Website. He wasn't messing with some power company's grid or reading an ex-girlfriend's e-mail.

Considering what a highly skilled hacker like himself is capable of, he felt he was hardly doing anything at all.

To Mark, information is meant and pictures are meant to be looked at. So he had taken all of the pictures and not just a few. So he was hacking a private database and it wasn't totally innocent.

But it wasn't a capital crime - and he felt he was serving the greater good.

Yes, to Mark, freedom of information was part of an unshakable moral code. It was an extension of his hacker's creed - if there's a wall you find a way to knock it down or crawl over it. If there's a fence, you cut your way through.

BEEP!

Yes, in Mark's mind he was fighting the good fight - and he wanted the information he was hacking worse than that couple seemed to want each other earlier.

The beep from his laptop signaling that this particular mission was done, Mark quickly made his exit.

He had more work to do that night - and he was really feeling like James Bond.

ONE HOUSE DOWN, TWO HOUSES TO GO.

HMMM! I CAN STILL SMELL THAT GIRL'S PERFUME IN THE AIR!

It took about 72 hours for Mark to realize what he'd done.

He hadn't thought about Facemash at all since his drunken evening and had spent his time studying, going to classes and hanging out with friends, like Eduardo.

He had simply considered Facemash a task to be completed. That's all.

After a meeting for one of his classes, Mark entered his dorm room at Kirkland to drop off his backpack and check his e-mails before heading down to the dining hall.

HOLY SHIT!

It was at that moment when he realized the impact of what he'd done.

Before he had left for the meeting, he had e-mailed the link to Facemash.com to a few friends in order to get their input. They had e-mailed their friends, who forwarded it to their friends, who forwarded it to their friends and it obviously picked up steam on it's own.

Mark's laptop was frozen because it had been acting as a server for Facemash.com and in under two hours, the site had logged 22,000 votes. Facemash was everywhere. Four hundred kids had gone onto the site in the past 30 minutes.

Unfortunately, for Mark, his site where you could compare two pictures of undergraduate girls had not just gone viral, but been forwarded to a dozen different e-mail lists. Someone had sent it to everyone involved with the Institute ofPolitics, which had over 100 members. Somone else had forwarded it to Fuerza Latino - the Latina Women's Issues Organization.

Someone else forwarded it to the Association of Black Women at Harvard and it had also gone to Harvard's "Crimson" newspaper and been linked to some of the house bulletin boards.

SHIT!

Mark knew this wasn't good and hadn't wanted the link to go out this way. He had wanted to get some opinions. Tweak it. Find out the legalities of downloading all those pictures. He might even have decided to never launch it.

But it was too late for that. All he could do was kill it and hope the damage done was minimal.

Mark did not know how things got this way or what was in store for him.

But as his laptop screen went blank, signaling he had succeeded in killing his creation, he was pretty sure about one thing. He had a strong feeling he was in big trouble.

Facemash made Mark known all throughout Harvard.

Popular wouldn't be the proper word, though, because many women were offended.

If Mark had trouble connecting with girls before, Facemash had just made it nearly impossible.

However, Mark's stunt would get a positive reaction from Tyler and Cameron Winklevoss - and their friend Divya Narendra.

They had been looking for a computer programmer to finish up a social networking site they had been working on for some time.

I'M NOT GOING TO FIND ANYBODY IN THE "CRIMSON"?

WHAT THE FUCK, MAN?

SORRY ABOUT THE SANDWICH. BUT LOOK AT THE HEADLINE.

The Winklevoss twins were used to excelling. They were Olympic-level in crew, got excellent grades and had a lot of money.

Their fraternity was the Porcellian, which was literally for people who wanted to learn how to rule the world.

Looking at the kid featured in the paper, they felt they had found someone to help them do that - or at least conquer the challenge of launching a website.

YEAH, I HEARD SOME OF THE GUYS AT THE PORC TALKING ABOUT THIS LAST NIGHT. IT GOT SHUT DOWN PRETTY FAST.

THE KID SHUT IT DOWN HIMSELF. WHEN HE CREATED THE SITE, HE DIDN'T EVEN REALIZE PEOPLE WERE GOING TO GET MAD, EVEN THOUGH ON HIS BLOG, HE TALKED ABOUT COMPARING GIRLS TO FARM ANIMALS.

WHO GOT MAD?

GIRLS. LOTS OF THEM. THE FEMINIST GROUPS ON CAMPUS SENT DOZENS OF LETTERS. AND THE UNIVERSITY'S MAD BECAUSE IT GOT 20,000 HITS IN 20 MINUTES AND CLOGGED UP THE UNIVERSITY'S BANDWIDTH. IT WAS A RIGHTEOUS MESS.

WOW.

YEAH. WOW.

The Winklevosses figured Mark would likely get probation but would need to restore his reputation - especially with women.

YOU DON'T COMPARE GIRLS TO FARM ANIMALS IF YOU'RE GETTING LAID REGULARLY.

THAT'S TRUE.

WE SHOULD TALK TO THIS KID.

BUT HE WROTE THAT COURSE MATCH THING, THAT ONLINE SCHEDULE, TO PICK YOUR CLASSES. AND IN HIGH SCHOOL, HE WAS SUPPOSEDLY SOME SORT OF MEGAHACKER.

Tyler understood but didn't care. Just like Cameron and he were really, really, really good at crew, this kid was really, really, really good at computers. He was perfect for what they needed him to do.

I ALREADY CALLED VICTOR. HE SAYS THE KID IS IN SOME COMPUTER CLASSES WITH HIM. HE WARNED ME THAT HE'S A LITTLE WEIRD, THOUGH.

WEIRD? HOW?

YOU KNOW, LIKE KIND OF SOCIALLY AUTISTIC.

WHAT'S THE KID'S NAME?

MARK ZUCKERBERG.

GO SEND HIM AN E-MAIL. LET'S SEE IF THIS ZUCKERBERG KID WANTS TO BE A PART OF HISTORY!

Eventually, Mark had to answer for Facemash in front of the ad board, Harvard's disciplinary organization.

Between having to wear a suit and tie and still not understanding why so many people were upset, it was like torture to him.

THAT WAS UNPLEASANT.

KIND OF LIKE A COLONOSCOPY.

It was earlier that morning that Mark had found himself forced to sit down in front of three deans and two computer experts, trying to explain himself.

He readily admitted his guilt, but was confused by the magnitude of the anger he had generated.

In Mark's mind, his actions had had a silver lining. He had eliminated some serious flaws in Harvard's computer system and volunteered to help fix the flaws.

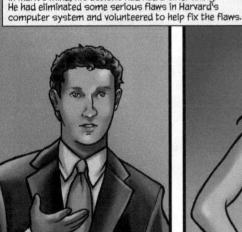

Mark's social awkwardness and confusion over the anger Facemash had unleashed was his greatest defense.

He truly didn't understand that the things that went on in his mind, the sort of talks you had with your buddies, didn't play well with the general public.

He truly didn't seem to understand why the idea of putting pictures of girls against farm animals would tick people off.

As a result, the gathered deans decided not to suspend or expel him over Facemash, but instead put him on probation - meaning he had to stay out of trouble for two years.

Mark's academic standing was intact, but his reputation was in tatters, especially with women.

However, he was now on the radar of three of the most popular and powerful kids on campus, as a printed-out e-mail confirmed.

I WANT TO SHOW YOU SOMETHING. WHAT DO YOU THINK OF THIS? YOU KNOW THESE GUYS?

I DON'T KNOW DIVYA, BUT I KNOW WHO THE WINKLEVOSS TWINS ARE. THEY'RE SENIORS. I THINK THEY LIVE IN THE QUAD. THEY ROW CREW.

ARE YOU GOING TO TALK TO THEM?

WHY NOT?

Eduardo was jealous over possibly losing his friend.

I'D SAY FUCK 'EM. YOU DON'T NEED THEM.

I DON'T KNOW. IT MIGHT BE - INTERESTING.

Tyler felt the Harvard Connection would act as an electronic hookup-helper, a super-slick connection between guys and girls.

It would serve as a one-stop shopping for that coed of your dreams.

And the key to it all was likely the geeky computer whiz motioning for Cameron and him to come over.

WE'RE GONNA CALL IT THE HARVARD CONNECTION.

Tyler tried to keep it simple at first. He explained the idea behind an online meeting place where Harvard guys and girls could find each other.

Then he got into the ideology behind the site - the thought that there was an inefficiency in the way people met each other and how Harvard Connection could bring people together based on their personalities rather than their proximity.

Mark seemed excited by the idea.

I LIKE THE CONCEPT OF A WEB SITE TO MEET GIRLS AND I'M SURE THE PROGRAMMING WON'T BE TOO DIFFICULT FOR ME. HOW FAR ALONG DID VICTOR GET WITH THE CODE?

YOU'RE WELCOME TO SEE FOR YOURSELF. WE'LL GIVE YOU THE PASSWORDS TO GO INSIDE VICTOR'S WORK.

YOU CAN EVEN DOWNLOAD THE CODE SO YOU CAN WORK ON IT FROM HOME IF YOU WANT. THERE'S ONLY ABOUT 10 HOURS OF WORK LEFT. SHOULDN'T BE HARD FOR YOU.

The more they talked about the computer aspect, the more into the project Mark seemed to get.

Tyler wanted Mark to know if he helped them make ConnectU a reality, he would be compensated.

IF THIS SITE IS SUCCESSFUL, WE'RE ALL GOING TO MAKE MONEY.

BUT MORE THAN MONEY, THIS IS GOING TO BE VERY COOL FOR ALL OF US. AND WE WANT YOU TO BE THE CENTERPIECE OF IT ALL. THIS WILL GET YOU BACK IN THE "CRIMSON" - BUT THIS TIME THE PAPER WILL BE PRAISING YOU, NOT TRASHING YOU.

Besides being offered partnership in the project and the possibility of making money, Tyler felt the possibility of Mark using the launch of their Web site to rehabilitate his image was too enticing to ignore.

Toss in the chance to show off his skills and meet the girls he wouldn't by hanging out at the computer lab and he was confident Mark couldn't resist.

ALL RIGHT, CAMERON! LOOKS LIKE WE HAVE A REASON TO CELEBRATE!

It was around Thanksgiving 2003, about a month after the Facemash incident, that Mark decided to tell Eduardo he was serious about developing an idea.

I THINK I'VE COME UP WITH SOMETHING.

I FEEL THERE'S REAL INTEREST IN STUDENTS CHECKING OUT CLASSMATES IN AN INFORMAL SETTING.

The huge interest in Facemash convinced Mark that the key part of the appeal was not seeing hot girls - there were a million web sites where people could do that - but seeing girls whom the kids at Harvard knew - sometimes personally.

SO IF PEOPLE WANT TO GO ONLINE AND CHECK OUT THEIR FRIENDS, WHY DON'T WE BUILD A WEB SITE THAT OFFERS EXACTLY THAT.

IT'LL BE AN ONLINE COMMUNITY OF FRIENDS - PICTURES, PROFILES, WHATEVER - THAT YOU CAN CLICK, VISIT, BROWSE AROUND.

BUT WE'LL MAKE IT EXCLUSIVE. YOU HAVE TO KNOW THE PEOPLE ON THE SITE TO GET INTO IT. IT'LL BE THE REAL WORLD - REAL SOCIAL CIRCLES - BUT PUT ONLINE BY THE PEOPLE IN THE SOCIAL CIRCLES THEMSELVES.

WE'LL MAKE IT WHERE PEOPLE PUT THEIR OWN PICTURES AND PROFILES UP, HOW OLD THEY ARE, WHAT THEY'RE INTERESTED IN,

WHAT CLASSES THEY'RE TAKING AND WHAT SORT OF RELATIONSHIP THEY'RE LOOKING FOR ONLINE.

I'M THINKING WE KEEP IT SIMPLE AND CALL IT THE FACEBOOK.

ISN'T THE SCHOOL WORKING ON SOME KIND OF ONLINE FACEBOOK?

As Eduardo listened, he liked the idea. It would be more exclusive, slicker and simply different from similar sites.

YEAH, BUT WHAT THEY'RE DOING ISN'T INTERACTIVE OR ANYTHING. IT'S NOT WHAT I'M TALKING ABOUT AT ALL. AND THE FACEBOOK IS A PRETTY GENERIC NAME.

I DON'T THINK IT MATTERS WHERE ELSE IT'S BEING USED.

Eduardo had no doubt Mark could pull off such a site. He just wondered where he had gotten the idea. He was pretty sure it wasn't the Winklevosses.

He recalled Mark's reaction immediately after their meeting.

IT'S LITTLE MORE THAN A DATING WEB SITE FOR GUYS WHO WANT TO TRY AND GET LAID - A HIGHBROW MATCH.COM.

I HAVEN'T DONE ANY WORK YET, BUT I'VE LOOKED AT THE SITE AND IT'S JUST NOT WORTH MY TIME.

HECK, EVEN MY MOST PATHETIC FRIENDS KNOW MORE ABOUT GETTING PEOPLE INTERESTED IN A WEB SITE THAN DIVYA AND THE WINKLEVOSSES.

BESIDES, I'M TOO BUSY WITH MY CLASSES TO WASTE TIME ON A DATING SITE JUST TO IMPRESS A COUPLE OF PORC JOCKS!

THEY THINK IT'LL REHABILITATE ME! I DON'T NEED TO REHABILITATE ANYTHING! I'VE BEATEN HARVARD'S COMPUTERS AND THE AD BOARD!

WHO ARE THEY TO TRY AND HARNESS MY ABILITIES? JUST A COUPLE OF JOCKS WHO THINK THEY RULE THE WORLD. MAYBE THEY RULE THE SOCIAL WORLD, BUT IN THE LAND OF WEB SITES AND COMPUTERS, I'M KING!

Eduardo wanted to be involved, but was wondering why Mark came to him instead of his roommate Dustin Moskovitz, another computer genius.

I THINK IT SOUNDS GREAT.

I'M IN.

IT IS GREAT. BUT WE'RE GOING TO NEED A LITTLE START-UP CASH TO RENT THE SERVERS AND GET IT ONLINE.

And there it was. Mark needed money to get his site going, knew Eduardo's family was wealthy and that Eduardo himself had made $300,000 selling oil futures.

Plus, this was a social site and now that Eduardo was in the Phoenix, he'd certainly help in that regard.

Eduardo not only had confidence in Mark's idea, he knew it would impress his father. Head of the Harvard Investment Association was one thing. Creating a popular web site would be another entirely.

HOW MUCH DO YOU THINK WE'LL NEED?

I THINK A THOUSAND DOLLARS TO START. THE THING IS, I DON'T REALLY HAVE A THOUSAND DOLLARS AT THE MOMENT, BUT IF YOU PUT UP WHAT YOU CAN RIGHT NOW, WE CAN GET THIS THING OFF THE GROUND.

I CAN HAVE A THOUSAND BUCKS IN 20 MINUTES. IT'LL JUST TAKE A SHORT TRIP TO THE BANK.

WE'LL SPLIT THE COMPANY 70/30. SEVENTY PERCENT FOR ME, THIRTY PERCENT FOR YOU. YOU CAN BE THE COMPANY'S CFO.

Eduardo thought that sounded fair, especially since he was confident they had all the ingredients for a successful Web site.

THIS IS GOING TO BE REALLY INTERESTING.

By January 14, 2004, Divya and the Winklevosses were becoming increasingly frustrated.

They had hoped to have ConnectU launched by the Holidays and now after seven weeks, 52 e-mails and a half-dozen phone calls between Mark and them, they seemed to be no closer to completion and were getting anxious.

If anything, they felt Mark was losing enthusiasm in the project.

LET'S LEAVE THE KID ALONE AND SEE IF HE GETS IT TOGETHER IN A FEW WEEKS.

AND IF HE DOESN'T GET IT TOGETHER IN A FEW WEEKS?

IF THAT HAPPENS, WE HAVE TO FIND OURSELVES A NEW PROGRAMMER. ONE THAT UNDERSTANDS THE BIG PICTURE. MAYBE MARK ZUCKERBERG DOESN'T GET IT AT ALL.

Unbeknownst to the Winklevosses, February 4, 2004 would turn out to be a huge day for Mark Zuckerberg and society.

I THOUGHT WE WERE SUPPOSED TO MEET AT NINE.

CAN'T TALK.

YOU HAVEN'T SLEPT YET, HAVE YOU?

WHY CAN'T YOU TALK?

Mark was in the type of pure laser focus mode every engineer understood.

He was working around the clock, day and night, and would not tolerate any distraction until he was done.

His friend was working so hard, Eduardo didn't even care when he noticed "A Mark Zuckerberg Production" at the bottom of every page he was working on. He realized Mark was giving his all.

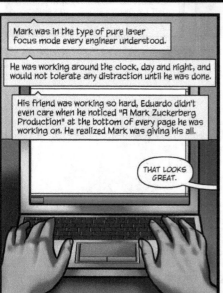

THAT LOOKS GREAT.

Mark had just figured out an addition that was going to make this all work. In big letters, your "sex" and what you were "looking for", your "relationship status" and what you were "interested" in - the resume items that were at the heart of the college experience - were displayed prominently.

What would drive the website was what drove life at college - sex. Getting it or not getting it. An undercurrent of sex drove people to pick certain classes or seats in the cafeteria - and it would drive this web-site.

OKAY. HERE WE GO.

Mark was ready. He wrote a simple e-mail, introducing the site linked in thefacebook.com, took a breath, hit a key and and sent out a mass e-mail and he was done.

After all the time and effort, their Web Site was out there. It was alive!

LET'S GET A DRINK! IT'S TIME TO CELEBRATE!

NO. I'M GOING TO STAY HERE.

YOU SURE? I HEAR THERE ARE SOME GIRLS COMING OVER TO THE PHOENIX LATER. THEY SENT THE FUCK TRUCK FOR 'EM.

YOU'RE GOING TO STAY HERE AND STARE AT THE COMPUTER SCREEN?

Eduardo got the feeling that at that moment, Mark viewed him as a distraction, like the sound of the radiators.

Mark still didn't answer. Just kept staring. It was a strange sight, but Eduardo decided not to judge his awkward friend.

Why should he? Mark had been working round the clock to get the facebook ready for this launch. If he wanted to sit by himself and stare, he'd earned the right.

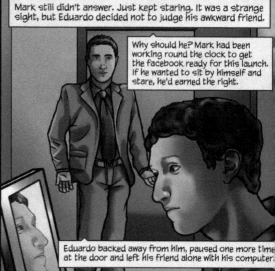

Eduardo backed away from him, paused one more time at the door and left his friend alone with his computer.

It was February 9, 2004 when the Winklevoss twins became aware of what Mark had accomplished.

WHAT IS IT WITH YOU AND THAT NEWSPAPER?

WHEN MARK E. ZUCKERBERG '06 GREW IMPATIENT WITH THE CREATION OF AN OFFICIAL HARVARD FACEBOOK, HE DECIDED TO TAKE MATTERS INTO HIS OWN HANDS.

HOLD ON! WHAT THE HELL IS THAT?

TODAY'S PAPER. LISTEN TO THIS. AFTER ABOUT A WEEK OF CODING, ZUCKERBERG LAUNCHED THEFACEBOOK.COM LAST WEDNESDAY AFTERNOON.

THE WEBSITE COMBINES ELEMENTS OF A STANDARD HOUSE FACEBOOK WITH EXTENSIVE PROFILE FEATURES THAT ALLOW STUDENTS TO SEARCH FOR OTHERS IN THEIR COURSES, SOCIAL ORGANIZATIONS AND HOUSES.

THIS IS CRAZY! HE LAUNCHED A WEBSITE?

HERE, THEY QUOTE HIM RIGHT IN THE ARTICLE. "EVERYONE'S BEEN TALKING A LOT ABOUT A UNIVERSAL FACEBOOK WITHIN HARVARD", ZUCKERBERG SAID.

"I THINK IT'S KIND OF SILLY THAT IT WOULD TAKE THE UNIVERSITY A COUPLE OF YEARS TO GET AROUND TO IT. I CAN DO IT BETTER THAN THEY CAN, AND I CAN DO IT IN A WEEK."

HE CAN DO IT IN A WEEK? HE'S BEEN PUTTING US OFF FOR TWO MONTHS! THAT HE'S BEEN TOO BUSY WITH CLASSES AND THE HOLIDAYS! HE'S BEEN LYING RIGHT TO OUR FACES!

I SHOT HIM AN E-MAIL LESS THAN 2 WEEKS AGO AND HE NEVER RESPONDED! I THOUGHT HE WAS BOGGED DOWN WITH SCHOOLWORK!

HE HAD TIME TO MAKE HIS OWN FUCKING WEB SITE, BUT HE COULDN'T FIND THE TIME TO GIVE US TEN HOURS OF CODING?

IT GETS WORSE. "AS OF YESTERDAY AFTERNOON, ZUCKERBERG SAID OVER 650 STUDENTS HAD REGISTERED TO USE THE FACEBOOK. HE SAID THAT HE ANTICIPATED THAT 900 STUDENTS WOULD HAVE JOINED THE SITE BY THE MORNING."

HOLY SHIT! THAT CAN'T BE TRUE! 900 KIDS IN 4 DAYS! ZUCKERBERG DOESN'T SEEM LIKE HE HAS FOUR FRIENDS, FROM WHAT I CAN TELL!

HOW THE HELL HAS HE LAUNCHED A WEBSITE AND GOTTEN THAT KIND OF RESPONSE IN 4 DAYS?!

I CHECKED THE SITE OUT AS SOON AS I READ THIS. IT'S TRUE - THE THING IS REALLY EXPLODING. YOU HAVE TO HAVE A HARVARD E-MAIL - AND THEN YOU GET TO UPLOAD YOUR PICTURE AND PERSONAL ACADEMIC INFO.

YOU CAN SEARCH FOR PEOPLE ACCORDING TO INTERESTS AND THEN WHEN YOU FIND YOUR FRIENDS YOU MAKE A NETWORK OUT OF THEM.

IT DOESN'T SOUND THE SAME AS HARVARD CONNECTION - BUT IT DOESN'T SOUND THAT DIFFERENT EITHER.

COULD MARK REALLY HAVE BEEN MEANING TO WORK ON OUR SITE - BUT GOTTEN CARRIED AWAY WITH HIS OWN?

NO! SORRY, THIS DOESN'T SEEM RIGHT. THIS SEEMS LIKE... THEFT.

FROM WHAT I HEAR, HE GOT FINANCING FROM ONE OF HIS BUDDIES, A BRAZILIAN KID NAMED EDUARDO SAVERIN. HE'S IN THE PHOENIX. MADE SOME MONEY TRADING STOCKS OVER THE SUMMER. NOW HE'S PART OWNER OF THE SITE.

I GUESS.

BECAUSE HE PAID FOR IT?

WELL, THAT EXPLAINS THE 900 IF THE KID'S IN THE PHOENIX. BUT IF HE NEEDED MONEY, WHY DIDN'T MARK COME TO US?

YEAH, HE KNEW WE WERE IN THE PORC. EVERYBODY KNOWS WHAT THAT MEANS. IF HE NEEDED MONEY, HE COULD HAVE MENTIONED THAT TO US!

UNLESS THE THING HE NEEDED CASH FOR WAS SOMETHING HE STOLE FROM US! UNLESS THE WEB SITE HE WAS WORKING ON HAD TO BE KEPT SECRET BECAUSE IT WAS TOO SIMILAR TO WHAT WE ASKED HIM TO DO!

YEAH, ASKED! WE CAN'T EVEN SAY HIRED, BECAUSE WE NEVER PAID HIM! THERE'S NO CONTRACT NO PAPERWORK, NOTHING BUT A HANDSHAKE!

FUCK! WHY DIDN'T WE WRITE SOMETHING UP? EVEN SOME BULLSHIT ONE PAGER? SOMETHING SIMPLE? WE JUST TRUSTED THE KID AND NOW HE'S FUCKED US OVER!

HE STALLED US! LED US ON! NOW HE'S LAUNCHED HIS OWN SITE WITH SIMILAR FEATURES!

HERE'S THE BEST PART, "ZUCKERBERG SAID THAT HE HOPED THE PRIVACY OPTIONS WOULD HELP TO RESTORE HIS REPUTATION FOLLOWING STUDENT OUTRAGE OVER FACEMASH.COM, A WEB SITE HE CREATED IN THE FALL SEMESTER. GOD *DAMN IT!*

THAT'S ALMOST THE EXACT SAME PITCH I GAVE MARK! THAT THE HARVARD CONNECTION WOULD RESTORE HIS REPUTATION! AND HE'S USING IT RIGHT THERE IN THE "CRIMSON"! IT'S LIKE HE'S MOCKING US!

HE STRUNG US ALONG FOR TWO MONTHS! ALL THROUGH THE HOLIDAYS AND WINTER PERIOD! ALL THE WHILE HE'S WORKING ON HIS OWN WEB SITE?

HE BLOWS US OFF - AND THEN BARELY TWO WEEKS LATER LAUNCHES HIS OWN SITE - THEFACEBOOK.COM? HE STEALS THE THUNDER AND THE ESSENCE OF OUR IDEA?

WHAT ARE WE GOING TO DO?

I'M NOT SURE - BUT I AM SURE I'M NOT GOING TO LET THAT FUCKING WEASEL GET AWAY WITH THIS!

FIRST, WE'RE GOING TO MAKE A PHONE CALL!

There is no one Tyler Winklevoss respected more than his father, a self-made multimillionaire who ran one of the most successful companies on Wall Street. Who better to advise him on his difficult situation?

YES, I KNOW HOW HARD YOU'VE WORKED. YOU'VE BEEN TALKING ABOUT THIS VENTURE SINCE 2002.

THERE ARE THINGS THAT SEEM REAL SIMILAR, DAD.

THIS ISN'T ABOUT MONEY. WHO KNOWS IF EITHER OF OUR SITES ARE EVER GOING TO MAKE ANY MONEY? BUT THIS ISN'T RIGHT. IT ISN'T FAIR.

THIS ISN'T THE WAY THE WORLD'S SUPPOSED TO WORK, DAD. YOU BROUGHT US UP BELIEVING THAT ORDER AND RULES MATTER. YOU WORK HARD AND YOU GET WHAT YOU DESERVE.

MAYBE IN MARK'S HACKER WORLD, THINGS ARE DIFFERENT. MAYBE HE FEELS YOU JUST DO WHATEVER THE HELL YOU WANT. YOU LAUNCH PRANK SITES LIKE FACEMASH.

YOU HACK INTO HARVARD'S COMPUTERS. YOU THUMB YOUR NOSE AT AUTHORITY AND MOCK PEOPLE IN THE PAGES OF THE "CRIMSON".

BUT THAT ISN'T WHAT YOU TAUGHT US WAS ACCEPTABLE DAD. AND IT'S NOT SUPPOSED TO BE WHAT HARVARD'S ABOUT. HARVARD'S A PLACE OF ORDER, RIGHT?

I'M GOING TO PUT YOU ON WITH MY IN-HOUSE COUNSEL.

GREAT! MAYBE IT'S NOT TOO LATE AND WE CAN STILL MAKE THIS RIGHT!

Shortly thereafter, Microsoft founder Bill Gates came to Harvard. Despite being an awkward speaker, his audience - made up mostly of engineering and computer geeks and a few economics majors with entrepreneurial aspirations - hung on his every word.

YOU KNOW WHY I DROPPED OUT OF SCHOOL? I HAD A TERRIBLE HABIT OF NOT GOING TO CLASSES!

HAHAHAHA

AI IS OUR FUTURE! THE NEXT BILL GATES IS OUT THERE - POSSIBLY IN THIS VERY ROOM!

DO I EVER REGRET LEAVING SCHOOL?

To someone like Mark, it was more than just listening to a legend. It was like getting advice from God.

Mark's seemingly cheerful reaction to Gates' school advice made Eduardo nervous.

Especially since Mark had been working so hard on their web site and had made it his top priority.

But dropping out wasn't an option for Eduardo. His father would throw a fit. Nothing was more important than education to his family.

WELL, THE GREAT THING ABOUT HARVARD IS THAT YOU COULD ALWAYS COME BACK AND FINISH.

Besides, Eduardo knew that to be a good businessman meant taking risks - but you didn't risk your entire future on something until you absolutely knew how it was going to make you rich.

Eduardo's future plans for the business and fascination with Mark's fascination with Gates was interrupted by a couple of decidedly female giggles behind him.

YOUR FRIEND - ISN'T THAT MARK ZUCKERBERG?

YOU KNOW MARK?

NO. BUT DIDN'T HE MAKE FACEBOOK?

YEAH. I MEAN, FACEBOOK, IT'S BOTH OF OURS - MINE AND HIS.

WOW. THAT'S REALLY COOL. MY NAME IS KELLY. THIS IS ALICE.

VERY NICE TO MEET YOU.

FACEBOOK ME WHEN YOU GET HOME. MAYBE WE CAN ALL GO OUT FOR A DRINK LATER.

People had dropped the "the" and were simply calling the site Facebook all over campus. And with 5,000 members in only two weeks, virtually the entire campus - 85% of the student body to be precise - had put up a profile for thefacebook. Eduardo soon noticed others pointing at Mark. The popularity of thefacebook combined with the press Mark had received from the "Crimson" had seemingly made him a celebrity. It was a role he was comfortable letting Mark have. He had no interest in being a celebrity - just a businessman. Of course, celebrity had it's perks.

Eduardo wanted to talk business after the Gates lecture - discuss ideas on how the company could make money. Mark had something else on his mind.

THOSE ASIAN CHICKS WERE PRETTY CUTE.

THAT COULD BE INTERESTING.

YEAH, AND THEY WANT TO MEET US LATER TONIGHT.

COULD BE - MARK, WHAT THE HELL IS THIS?!

Eduardo had discovered what was obviously a legal letter from the Winklevoss twins. The words TheFacebook were pretty hard to miss. It looked serious - including words like "DAMAGES" and "MISAPPROPRIATED", accused Mark of stealing their idea and demanded TheFacebook be shut down.

WHEN DID YOU GET IT?!

I THINK THEY CALL IT A CEASE-AND-DESIST LETTER. WHAT WERE THE GIRLS' NAMES? I LIKED THE SHORT ONE.

A WEEK AGO. RIGHT AFTER WE LAUNCHED THE SITE. THEY ALSO SENT AN E-MAIL SAYING THEY WERE GOING TO APPEAL TO THE SCHOOL, TOO. THAT I HAD VIOLATED HARVARD'S CODE OF ETHICS.

JESUS CHRIST!

RELAX. I TALKED TO A THREE-ONE AT THE LAW SCHOOL. I SENT LETTER BACK. AND ANOTHER ONE TO THE SCHOOL. UNDER THAT NEXT BOOK.

Mark's response letter to Harvard had stated, in no uncertain terms that The Facebook was not related in any way to the tiny bit of work he'd done for the Winklevosses. Mark added that he had felt fooled by the twins because of the initial meeting, that it was the twins that had misrepresented what they wanted him to do and that he hadn't led them on at all. Mark concluded that: He was appalled to find himself "threatened" by the twins because of a few meetings and e-mails, saw their claims as an "annoyance" and something he was "shrugging off", that the twins were simply jealous he had made something successful.

Mark's confidence helped calm Eduardo down. After all, he was the one who knew about coding and had met with the twins so Eduardo decided to talk about more pleasant and pressing things.

IT'S LIKE ONE FURNITURE MAKER TRYING TO SUE SOMEONE FOR DESIGNING A NEW KIND OF CHAIR. THERE'S THOUSANDS OF DIFFERENT TYPES OF CHAIRS AND MAKING ONE DOESN'T GIVE YOU THE RIGHT TO OWN THEM ALL.

THEIR NAMES WERE KELLY AND ALICE.

It was that night that Eduardo told Mark he wanted to start making some real money. Mark seemed content to only generate enough money to run the site. Eduardo thought differently. It was that night Eduardo became confident that both Mark and he were going to get rich from Facebook.

That night was when they both realized they already had groupies and that Eduardo had been dead wrong - a computer program could get you laid. Eduardo felt this was the first of countless experiences Mark and he would share - that they were now an unbeatable, inseparable team.

During this time period, the Winklevoss twins kept running into administrators at Harvard who were sympathetic to their complaints but declared they couldn't do anything.

Next, they contacted Mark in hopes of meeting with him directly to resolve the situation. He agreed to meet - but only with Cameron for some reason and the meeting fell through.

Neither twin felt they could trust him anymore anyway. So they pulled every connection they could find - from the Porc to their family to get an audience with the ultimate authority on campus - Harvard President Larry Summers.

The Winklevosses presented Summers with a ten-page complaint outlining their association with Mark Zuckerberg, from summaries of conversations to printed-out e-mails.

It was a lot of work and they were happy it had made it to the President's desk. Summers did not share their joy. Instead, he looked at them with pure distaste in his eyes.

WHY ARE YOU HERE?

I THINK IT'S PRETTY SELF-EXPLANATORY. MARK STOLE OUR IDEA.

SO WHAT DO YOU WANT ME TO DO ABOUT IT?

IT'S AGAINST UNIVERSITY RULES TO STEAL FROM ANOTHER STUDENT. IF MARK HAD GONE INTO OUR DORM ROOM AND TAKEN OUR COMPUTER, YOU WOULD KICK HIM OUT OF SCHOOL.

WELL, HE'S DONE SOMETHING MUCH WORSE. HE'S TAKEN OUR IDEA AND OUR WORK - AND THE UNIVERSITY SHOULD STEP IN AND UPHOLD THE HARVARD CODE OF ETHICS.

I'VE READ YOUR COMPLAINT. AND I'VE READ MARK'S RESPONSE. I DON'T SEE THIS AS A UNIVERSITY ISSUE.

BUT THERE'S A CODE OF ETHICS! THERE'S AN HONOR CODE! WHAT GOOD IS A CODE IF IT DOESN'T HAVE ANY TEETH?!

YOU ENTERED INTO A CODE OF ETHICS WITH THE UNIVERSITY - NOT EACH OTHER. THIS ISSUE IS BETWEEN YOU GUYS AND MARK ZUCKERBERG.

BUT THE UNIVERSITY HAS A RESPONSIBILITY TO UPHOLD THE HONOR CODE!

THE UNIVERSITY ISN'T EQUIPPED TO HANDLE A SITUATION LIKE THIS.

WHAT DO YOU PROPOSE WE DO ABOUT IT?

WORK IT OUT WITH HIM. OR FIND SOME OTHER WAY TO DEAL WITH IT, AS A LEGAL ISSUE.

Tyler was devastated that the options Summers was offering was a face-to-face with Mark - who had shown he would lie to their faces - or a lawsuit, which seemed even more horrible.

Summers was telling them that they were on their own. The administration was washing it's hands of the whole thing.

TheFacebook was a popular campus phenomenon, Mark was getting famous, his web site was growing daily - and the president was basically endorsing it's success.

Tyler was crestfallen as he realized he and his brother's only option left was going after Mark themselves.

As he left the meeting, he felt he was leaving his innocence behind.

Because he was convinced that Mark Zuckerberg had stolen his idea. Yet Harvard, a place he grew up respecting was going to let him get away with it.

In March 2004, Sean Parker would become aware of Mark and his creation - and neither would ever be the same again.

Parker was living in a house full of Stanford students, which is ironic because he had never gone to college there or anywhere else. He was already a legend in his early 20s - having co-created two wildly successful companies - Napster and Plaxo.

Both those ventures had ended badly for Sean Parker and many blamed his foolish, youthful mistakes for his downfall. But he regretted nothing.

Parker was already determined to find his third success story. This time he would do it right and would settle for nothing less than a home run. Parker had decided the next big thing would be social networks. He decided Friendster was a dating site and MySpace was a branding tool. He decided that he would find something completely different that would blow them and all the others away.

He was setting the bar high. If it wasn't a billion dollar company eventually - his own YouTube or Google - it wasn't worth his time.

MOTHER OF GOD.

One of his roommates had left his Facebook page open. Parker immediately realized it was what he was looking for - fluid and simple and beautiful. Once he saw the words, "A Mark Zuckerberg Production" at the bottom of the page, he decided he would Google him, find out everything about him. Then he was going to contact and meet Mark Zuckerberg and see how good he really was.

It was a few weeks later in April and and Eduardo was not in a good mood. Mark and he were in New York on business, yet he felt Mark wasn't taking it seriously. They were staying with friends instead of a hotel - but Eduardo had picked up the travel and all the food and taxi bills.

Everything was being paid out of thefacebook's bankroll, the quickly dwindling thousand dollars that Eduardo had put in back in January. So he felt Mark should have been treating the trip as serious business.

COME ON, EDUARDO! DO YOU THINK THEY'RE REALLY GOING TO CARD US? HERE?

But he'd done nothing of the sort. Eduardo had set up several meetings with potential advertisers, none of the meetings had gone particularly well and it hadn't helped that Mark had slept through about half of them and had spent the other half sitting silently while Eduardo tried to pick up all the slack.

Though everyone seemed impressed by the number of people they'd gotten to sign up to thefacebook - over 75,000 at that point - nobody was willing to put any significant money into placing ads on the network. They just didn't get it - and advertising on the internet was a dicey proposition to begin with.

Eduardo felt if Mark had taken things a bit more seriously, things would have gone a little better.

I mean, here they were at "66" one of the fanciest new restaurants in New York to discuss business, and Mark was sitting in his usual fleece hoodie, with his flip-flops bouncing off each other under the table.

But as miffed as Eduardo was at Mark, he was concerned about who they were meeting more. A quick internet search had convinced him that the man they were going to meet was a typical Silicon Valley animal, a serial entrepreneur who'd crashed out of two of the biggest internet companies in pretty spectacular fashion. Eduardo felt he was a wild man, a little dangerous and was unsure what he wanted from them.

SEAN PARKER. YOU MUST BE EDUARDO AND KELLY. AND, OF COURSE, MARK.

Eduardo immediately sensed virtual idol worship going on. To him, it's like Mark was looking into the eyes of a god.

Of course, Eduardo should have realized it earlier. Napster was the ultimate geek accomplishment, a battle that had been fought by hackers on the biggest stage of all. Ultimately, the hackers had lost. But that didn't change the fact that it was the biggest hack in history. And Sean Parker had survived that and gone on to Plaxo, made a name for himself a second time.

Sean's energy level was high as he told numerous stories. About Napster, the battles he had fought. About Plaxo and the even uglier battles he'd barely survived.

He talked about life in Silicon Valley. Parties at Stanford and down in LA. Friends who had become billionaires and others who were still searching for that big hit. Sean was painting a real exciting picture - and Mark was eating it all up. Eduardo thought Mark looked like he was about to run out of the restaurant and book a plane ticket to California.

SO, HOW ARE YOU GUYS PROGRESSING WITH THEFACEBOOK?

WELL, WE'RE NOW IN TWENTY-NINE SCHOOLS -

MARK, WHAT ARE THE STRATEGIES YOU'RE USING TO GET DIFFERENT SCHOOLS TO SIGN UP?

WELL, FOR EXAMPLE, BAYLOR TOLD US AT FIRST THEY DIDN'T WANT TO ADOPT THEFACEBOOK, BECAUSE THEY HAD A SOCIAL NETWORK OF THEIR OWN, RIGHT?

SO INSTEAD OF ATTACKING BAYLOR HEAD ON, WE MADE A LIST OF ALL THE SCHOOLS WITHIN A 100-MILE RADIUS OF IT AND DROPPED THEFACEBOOK INTO THOSE SCHOOLS FIRST.

PRETTY SOON ALL THE KIDS AT BAYLOR WERE SEEING ALL THEIR FRIENDS ON THE WEB SITE AND THEY PRACTICALLY BEGGED FOR THEFACEBOOK ON THEIR CAMPUS. WITHIN DAYS, THE BAYLOR SOCIAL WEB SITE WAS HISTORY!

After that tale, Sean let Mark know that after an article on "thefacebook.com craze" sweeping through campus, 85 percent of Stanford had joined thefacebook within twenty-four hours.

Dinner went by quickly. Mark was thrilled Sean was reading up on him. Sean seemed happy Mark was a fan. They were both computer savvy, only Sean was far from a geek. He was a showman, and was very good at what he did.

So, after dinner, with Kelly and Sean gone to a party, and Eduardo trying to raise a cab, he tried to break the spell Sean Parker seemed to have over his partner and friend.

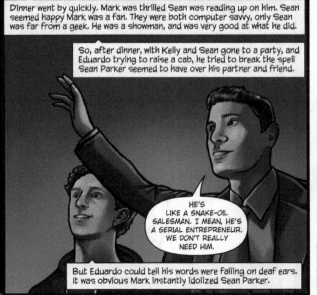

HE'S LIKE A SNAKE-OIL SALESMAN. I MEAN, HE'S A SERIAL ENTREPRENEUR. WE DON'T REALLY NEED HIM.

But Eduardo could tell his words were falling on deaf ears. It was obvious Mark instantly idolized Sean Parker.

Eduardo convinced himself it didn't matter at that moment. Sean Parker didn't have real money to give them and thefacebook needed money, if they were going to upgrade their servers and hire a couple of interns to keep up with the ever-increasing number of users.

Which is why the next day Eduardo was going to open a new bank account and put ten thousand more dollars he had freed up into the company's account. Mark didn't have any funds of his own, so they would have to rely on Eduardo's money a bit longer.

Even back at Harvard, Eduardo thought Sean probably did have some major connections to Venture Capital. However, Mark's repeated disinterest in money reassured him on that front. To Mark, the Web site was still primarily about fun and being cool.

Which is why Mark didn't find Eduardo's desire to get advertisers cool - and why he was confident he wouldn't find VCs cool, either. Guys in suits and ties offering money, they could never be cool - so Eduardo was confident that VC's they met or that Sean Parker introduced them to could never be cool, either.

Still, Eduardo couldn't help worrying that to Mark, Sean Parker was friends or not. But he put it out of his mind. Everything was going so well. Everyone loved thefacebook.

Sooner or later, they'd find a way to make money off it, with or without Sean Parker. Everyone was taking notice of their Web site and it was only a time before deep pockets came calling that could afford far more than a dinner at a fancy New York restaurant. Eduardo could not have known how right he would be.

As the Harvard spring semester of 2004 drew to a close, VCs were tracking both Mark and him down on campus at an almost alarming frequency. Reps from almost all the major software and internet companies were approaching them as well.

Guys in suits were approaching them in the campus dining hall and the library. One determined rep even waited for three hours outside Mark's dorm until he arrived, hoping for a chance to speak to him.

YUP. IT'S ANOTHER ONE.

YOU'RE SHITTING ME.

I SHIT YOU NOT.

Even with Dustin Moskovitz and Chris Hughes - two other computer whizzes brought on board by Mark - thefacebook was quickly becoming a full-time job for everyone.

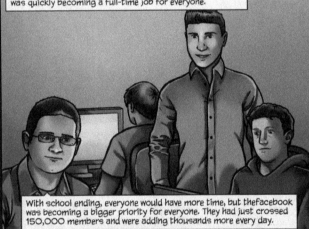

With school ending, everyone would have more time, but thefacebook was becoming a bigger priority for everyone. They had just crossed 150,000 members and were adding thousands more every day.

Though the attention they were all getting from thefacebook was great, they weren't being offered any real money yet.

Yet they had to find some way to pay for the rapidly growing server costs, plus the upkeep and maintenance needed now that the site was being used by so many people, 24 hours a day.

Eduardo began running free test ads for a handful of big national companies and also sold some ads to a few Harvard organizations. It wasn't a lot, but it helped.

Knowing they needed to move the business along in terms of structure, Mark and Eduardo officially incorporated themselves on April 13, 2004, legally creating TheFacebook LLC, registered in Florida, where Eduardo's family lived.

On paper, the ownership of the company would be the same as everyone agreed upon in Mark's dorm room: 65 percent ownership for Mark; 30 percent for Eduardo and 5 percent for Dustin. Chris would get some percentage decided on in the future.

In any event, these documents made the company seem real - even though Facebook wasn't making any real money yet.

With the documents signed and thefacebook growing rapidly, the decision about what to do when the school year ended in a few weeks was a difficult one. Mark and Eduardo were both just going through the motions of looking for summer jobs.

Mark couldn't find anything he was psyched about.

Meanwhile, Eduardo's Phoenix conections and family's friends had managed to land a pretty prestigious internship at a New York investment bank.

NEW YORK CITY

Eduardo kept debating the internship with his father but it was obvious which way he was leaning.

YES, THEFACEBOOK IS GROWING AND INCREDIBLY POPULAR, BUT IT'S STILL NOT MAKING YOU ANY MONEY.

I KNOW THAT, DAD.

THIS INTERNSHIP IS A RESPECTABLE JOB! AN AMAZING OPPORTUNITY! MOST OF THE ADVERTISERS YOU'RE CHASING ARE BASED IN NEW YORK, ANYWAY.

SO DOESN'T IT MAKE SENSE FOR YOU TO TAKE THE INTERNSHIP AND WORK ON THEFACEBOOK DURING YOUR SPARE TIME?

YOU'VE GOT A POINT, DAD. YOU'RE MAKING SENSE.

Before Eduardo could even bring up the internship with Mark, He had a bombshell of his own. Wirehog would be like a bastard child of Napster and facebook, Mark explained, and a couple of other computer programming whizzes - Adam D'Angelo, his high school friend with whom he'd invented Synapse, and Andrew McCollum, a classmate and fellow CS major would be helping him. A sort of file-sharing program with a social network feel. Wirehog would be downloadable software that would allow people to share anything from music to pictures to video with friends.

THEFACEBOOK IS STILL MY PRIORITY, BUT I'VE BEEN DEVELOPING A SIDE PROJECT CALLED WIREHOG.

The idea was when Mark was finished with Wirehog, he'd merge it into thefacebook as an application. Meanwhile, both he and Dustin would continue to upgrade thefacebook.

Mark said he hoped to increase the number of schools using the Web site from about 30 to over 100 by the end of the summer.

Combined with the Wirehog project, Mark had certainly put enormous expectations on himself. But Mark seemed more thrilled and excited than overwhelmed by it.

Mark's stated intention to divide his time between the two projects made Eduardo's decision to take the internship a little easier.

It was then that Mark dropped an unexpected bombshell, one that made the Wirehog project look trivial.

Eduardo got it. Mark wanted to work on thefacebook and Wirehog in Silicon Valley - a land of legend to people like Mark where all his heroes had made their mark.

I'VE COME TO THE CONCLUSION THAT CALIFORNIA IS WHERE I SHOULD BE FOR THE NEXT FEW MONTHS.

ANDREW'S GOT A JOB LINED UP AT EA SPORTS IN SILICON VALLEY AND ADAM IS COMING AS WELL. WE'VE FOUND A CHEAP SUBLET ON A STREET CALLED LA JENNIFER WAY IN PALO ALTO, NEAR THE STANFORD CAMPUS. IT'S THE PERFECT PLAN.

DUSTIN'LL COME ALONG, WE'LL SET UP SHOTS IN THE RENTAL HOUSE AND THEFACEBOOK AND WIREHOG WILL BE RIGHT WHERE THEY BELONG - IN THE EPICENTER OF AN ONLINE WORLD.

Eduardo did not like Mark's plan - did not like the idea of him moving at all. Not only was California as far away from New York as you could get, but it could also be a dangerous and seductive place. While Eduardo was in New York chasing advertisers, guys in suits like the VCs that always hounded them in class lately would now be hounding Mark in greater numbers.

Worse, in Eduardo's mind, than the guys in suits were the guys like Sean Parker - who knew exactly the buttons to push with guys like Mark. Besides, he worried, the plan had always been for Mark and Dustin to be the programmers while Eduardo played the businessman. If they separated, how was Eduardo going to guide the business like they agreed?

LOOK, THERE'S NO REASON WE CAN'T WORK FROM TWO CITIES AT ONCE. DUSTIN AND I'LL CONTINUE PROGRAMMING AND YOU HANDLE FINANCES.

SPEAKING OF WHICH, WE'RE GOING TO HAVE TO HIRE A COUPLE INTERNS IF WE WANT TO GET TO 100 SCHOOLS BY THE END OF THE SUMMER.

ANYWAY, WE'RE DONE DEBATING THE ISSUE. I'VE MADE MY DECISION AND YOU'VE ACCEPTED YOUR INTERNSHIP. WE'LL JUST HAVE TO FIND A WAY TO MAKE IT WORK.

Eduardo, like Mark, was growing tired of the VCs chasing them around

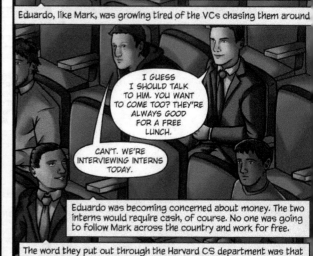

I GUESS I SHOULD TALK TO HIM. YOU WANT TO COME TOO? THEY'RE ALWAYS GOOD FOR A FREE LUNCH.

CAN'T. WE'RE INTERVIEWING INTERNS TODAY.

Eduardo was becoming concerned about money. The two interns would require cash, of course. No one was going to follow Mark across the country and work for free.

The word they put out through the Harvard CS department was that they were going to pay each intern about eight thousand for the summer, along with room and board at their La Jennifer Way Sublet.

It seemed a lot considering the company wasn't making any money yet, but Eduardo had agreed to fund the project again, out of his investment earnings. In a few days, he planned to open a new Bank of America account in the company's name. He'd freed up $18,000 to deposit into the account and he was going to give Mark a package of blank checks to fund their operation in California. As the man in charge of the business side of the operation, it seemed the right thing to do.

SHOULD BE INTERESTING.

AFTER I'M DONE WITH THIS BOZO, I'LL COME BY AND HELP OUT WITH THE INTERNS.

After Mark left for California, Eduardo became confident they could make it all work. He comforted himself with the knowledge that in three short months they'd all be back at school. Eduardo would be entering his senior year, Mark his junior. Life would continue. Maybe they'd be rich by then. Or they'd still be watching their company grow. Maybe Mark would make some contacts in Silicon Valley.

No matter what happened, they were both clearly different than when they began the company and Eduardo had no doubt that the future was going to be great. He pushed his previous worries out of his mind, because that's what a team player did. There was no need to worry or be paranoid.

After all, he asked himself, how much could go wrong in a handful of months?

Another benefit of going to California is that Mark could leave the annoyances and unpleasant parts of the recent past behind him, at least temporarily.

For example, right near the end of the semester, Cameron Winklevoss spotted him coming out of a campus party.

MARK! DON'T RUN! I JUST WANT TO TALK! MARK!

But soon after landing in California, fate seemed to guide him to a man who would play a large role in thefacebook's future, when he went for a walk and happened to run into...

SEAN PARKER?

THIS IS A BIZARRE COINCIDENCE.

YEAH, THESE ARE MY ROOMMATES. WE JUST MOVED A HALF BLOCK UP THE STREET FOR THE SUMMER.

Sean thought this meeting was fate, the latest in a series of fortuitous events that were making up his life. He had worked so hard to track down Mark in New York and now they were together by chance in California.

They had exchanged a couple e-mails and had plans to get together at an event in Vegas fall through since then. But this was better - almost a perfect opportunity.

YEAH? I'VE BEEN LIVING WITH MY GIRLFRIEND, BUT NOW THAT THE SEMESTER'S OVER I'LL BE STAYING WITH HER AT HER PARENTS' FOR A COUPLE OF DAYS, BUT AFTER THAT I'LL BE HOMELESS.

Mark could barely hide his joy. He had come all the way to Silicon Valley because it seemed the right place to build an internet company. So what could be better than having an adviser who'd already launched two of the most talked-about companies in town crashing in the same house?

Sean had wanted to get involved with thefacebook the second he'd seen it. Now he was going to be living with the brain behind it.

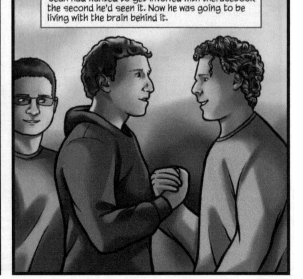

YOU GUYS COULD USE A LESSON ON THE FINER WAYS OF LIVING LIFE. WE'RE BUILDING A SOCIAL NETWORK. YOU SHOULD AT LEAST LEARN WHAT IT MEANS TO BE SOCIAL.

All kidding aside, Sean was beginning to admire the hell out of Mark. Besides obviously being a genius, Sean could tell Mark had the drive, stamina and unique ability to focus that was necessary to succeed in a big way.

Sean felt watching Mark program at four in the morning - every morning - that Mark had the makings of one of the truly great Silicon Valley success stories.

Sean was equally pleased that Mark had assembled what seemed to be the perfect engineering soldiers. A top-notch crew.

What was confusing was that the one person he didn't see in the house was Eduardo.

This struck him as odd since he had been introduced as the titular business head of thefacebook and had made it clear - several times - that he was going to be running all business aspects of the Web site - yet it looked to Sean that Eduardo wasn't involved in the day-to-day workings of thefacebook at all.

When Mark had told him Eduardo had accepted an internship in New York it set off alarms in Sean's head. Having been a part of two major companies and having seen numerous other successes and failures - he knew the most important things were the dedication and ambition of the founders. To really succeed, you had to live and breathe the project every minute of every day.

Eduardo saw himself as a businessman, but Sean felt Silicon Valley wasn't about business. It was a war and to survive you had to do things that weren't taught in any business class. None of the real success stories - from him to Bill Gates - had gotten where they were by taking classes. They all came out here, usually with only a duffel bag to call their own. Sean didn't even have that. Much of his stuff was in storage. But Eduardo wasn't here. Mark was. So Sean put Eduardo out of his mind.

LOOK, I REALLY FEEL THIS IS THE BILLION-DOLLAR PROJECT I'VE BEEN LOOKING FOR.

I'M A ROCK STAR IN THIS TOWN, BUT I THINK YOU'LL BE BIGGER THAN ME EVENTUALLY.

YOU'RE GOING TO BE THE TOAST OF THE TOWN AND I'M GOING TO SHOW YOU HOW TO GET AND ENJOY ALL OF IT.

Sean had already figured and slightly regretted that Eduardo was going to miss out on the next stage of the company. The kid had been at the right place at the right time - but the place had changed and time was moving forward at the speed of light. Eduardo might try to hang on, but in Sean's mind he was already showing he didn't have what it took.

Ironically, Eduardo would quit his internship on the first day - minutes after receiving his first stack of stock valuations to analyze.

He decided then and there that he wasn't going to become a real businessman like his father by neglecting the business he and Mark had co-founded in the dorms.

He decided to push himself as hard as possible. He spent at least 10 hours a day that summer hitting the pavement and taking meetings with advertisers, potential investors, software makers and basically anyone who was interested in thefacebook, for whatever reason.

Despite his hard work, Eduardo was becoming anxious about thefacebook, wondering how things were going in California with Mark and their team - and why they weren't calling more often.

He became more concerned every time he talked to Mark and heard about another milestone, party or dinner he had missed by being in New York.

So Eduardo was excited when Mark told him Sean had gotten them invited to a big charity bash.

YEAH, MAN. YOU HAVE TO COME. ALL THE BIG-SHOT ENTREPRENEURS ARE GOING TO BE THERE. IT'S GONNA BE A BLAST- PLUS, YOU'LL GET THE OPPORTUNITY TO MEET WITH MORE INVESTOR TYPES, VCS, MAJOR SILICON VALLEY PLAYERS AND EVEN SOME INTERNET CELEBS.

SEAN'S ALREADY TAKEN US TO A BUNCH OF COOL PARTIES LIKE THIS. IT'S REALLY THE BEST THE AREA HAS TO OFFER - THE STANFORD SUMMER SCENE, THE SAN FRANCISCO HIGH-TECH GROOVE.

HE'S EVEN TAKEN US DOWN TO LA FOR SOME BIG HOLLYWOOD BASHES.

SEAN KNOWS EVERYBODY, MAN AND EVERYBODY KNOWS SEAN. AND THROUGH HIM, THEY'RE GETTING TO KNOW ME AND GET EXCITED BY THEFACEBOOK!

YEAH. I'VE GOT GOOD NEWS, TOO. I'M MAKING SOME REAL PROGRESS WITH ADVERTISERS. I LANDED A DEAL WITH Y2M AND SOME OTHER BIG PLAYERS HAVE BEEN MAKING SOME IMPRESSIVE PROMISES.

Mark's lack of enthusiasm regarding his efforts hurt Eduardo a bit, but he realized he was probably tired. Mark was working round the clock adding new features and signing up more schools.

GOOD. THAT'S GOOD.

It looked like they would pass 500,000 members by the end of August, which was spectacular. But such impressive growth created new problems.

Even if he wasn't a little concerned or jealous, solving those problems was a good enough reason for Eduardo to justify flying out to California.

They were going to need money soon. The company was still running off of the $18,000 he had deposited into the Bank of America account, via the blank checks he'd given Mark when he'd opened the account. The advertising money that was coming in wasn't going to be enough to keep up with the demand - 500,000 users would burn a lot of server space. And pretty soon, two interns would not be enough to keep the company running. They'd have to hire real employees, get a real office, hire more lawyers, etc. All of these things, Eduardo was prepared to discuss - as soon as he could get Mark alone. It wasn't stuff he felt Sean needed to hear about, because Eduardo felt it wasn't stuff that concerned Mark's houseguest - no matter how many cool parties he took them to.

HEY, WHAT DID YOU EXPECT? I JUST BOUGHT IT ON CRAIGSLIST A COUPLE DAYS AGO. IT DOESN'T EVEN HAVE A KEY. YOU HAVE TO FIDGET WITH THE IGNITION TO START IT.

WELL, AT LEAST YOU DON'T HAVE TO WORRY ABOUT ANYBODY STEALING IT!

SEAN'S MEETING IS THERE. HE'S GOT A VIP TABLE RESERVED.

COOL.

OKAY. LISTEN, MARK, I CLOSED THE Y2M DEAL AND I THINK I'M MAKING PROGRESS WITH OTHER POTENTIAL ADVERTISERS.

I'VE ALSO GOT SOME IDEAS FOR GETTING MORE FROM LOCAL ADVERTISERS IN EACH OF THEFACEBOOK LOCATIONS.

GOOD.

AND KELLY'S BEEN ACTING CRAZY. SHE LEFT ME TWELVE MESSAGES DURING THE FLIGHT FROM NEW YORK!

SO HOW'VE YOU BEEN MAKING OUT THE PAST MONTH? HOW ARE THE INTERNS AND PARKER WORKING OUT? IS THE SILICON VALLEY SCENE EVERYTHING YOU THOUGHT IT WOULD BE?

WOW.

IT'S BEEN INTERESTING.

WAIT! YOU KIDS THINK YOU'RE GETTING HERE?! THIS MAY BE SAN FRANCISCO, BUT EVEN WE HAVE STANDARDS!

THERE SHOULD BE 3 VIP RESERVATIONS UNDER THE NAME MARK ZUCKERBERG.

THE ONE KID SAYS THERE SHOULD BE THREE VIP RESERVATIONS, UNDER THE NAME MARK ZUCKERBERG? THEY DO?! SORRY, GUYS. GO RIGHT IN.

OVER HERE!

THE LAST TIME I WAS HERE, I WAS WITH THE FOUNDERS OF PAYPAL.

While Sean tried to impress everyone with his Silicon Valley adventures, Mark and Eduardo were distracted by a gorgeous brunette who was seated at an adjoining table of Victoria's Secret models. Mark looked like a deer caught in the headlights - but what wonderful headlights they were.

THE ONLY THING THAT BOTHERS ME ABOUT THE SITE IS THE "THE" IN THE NAME. IT'S UNNECESSARY. I HATE UNNECESSARY THINGS.

The next thing Mark knew, he was going home with a Victoria's Secret model. Eduardo realized that if someone as socially awkward like Mark could score on that magnitude, it was becoming increasingly clear that thefacebook was going to be the biggest thing in the world.

Things only got more insane after that. Sean had set up a large number of dinners, meetings, and cocktail hours for the time Eduardo was there - with VCs, reps and anyone who seemed interested in thefacebook.

Yes, a lot of people were interested and offers involving many millions were being whispered in their ears.

The wining and dining was extremely excessive. They were brought to the nicest, most expensive restaurants in San Francisco. Often, the interested parties sent limos for them, or had them picked up in SUVs.

And some decided to entice them with large gifts.

SORRY WE'RE LATE. I JUST GOT A CRAP CAR FROM CRAIGSLIST. I HAD A HARD TIME GETTING IT TO START, AND THAT'S WHY WE'RE LATE.

WHY DON'T I BUY YOU A SUV?

Everyone knew the guy was serious and that Mark would soon have a new car.

The weirdest meeting was when Mark and Eduardo talked business for a few hours on the yacht of one of the original founders of Sun Microsystems and were then presented lunch.

On the tray in front of them was a weird looking meat. They were both afraid to ask what it was, but didn't have to.

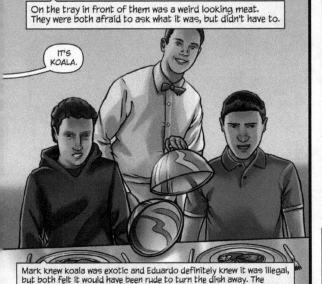

IT'S KOALA.

Mark knew koala was exotic and Eduardo definitely knew it was illegal, but both felt it would have been rude to turn the dish away. The controversy over Mark dining on koala persists to the present day.

As Eduardo flew home, he was happy and confident. He had gotten a taste of what living like a king was like and even been offered numbers that would make that lifestyle an everyday reality. No matter how insane the numbers got, he knew they weren't going to sell thefacebook. It was going to be worth a lot more in the future. They were closing in on 500,000 members and it was growing every day.

Despite the fact they were getting into serious debt and were barely being kept alive by the $18,000 he'd invested in the bank account. He didn't want to sell and knew Mark didn't, either. Sean Parker? Eduardo considered him an advisor and without a say in the company's future, which he felt was practically limitless.

Eduardo was on an emotional high after his trip to California and he was happy about the progress he was making back in New York.

YEAH, IT LOOKS LIKE Y2M IS A DONE DEAL, MARK! I'VE GOT A BUNCH OF OTHER ADVERTISERS LINED UP, TOO!

To say Mark seemed unappreciative of Eduardo's hard work in New York would be an understatement.

YEAH, THAT'S COOL. DUDE, YOU WOULD NOT BELIEVE THE PARTY SEAN BROUGHT US TO LAST NIGHT. THERE WAS A TON OF STANFORD SORORITY GIRLS AND EVEN MORE JAGERMEISTER.

YOU SHOULD REALLY MOVE OUT HERE, MAN. THIS IS WHERE IT'S ALL HAPPENING.

THE COMPUTER CODING, NETWORKING WITH POTENTIAL INVESTORS, MEETINGS WITH VCS AND SOFTWARE HONCHOS - I MEAN, YOU'RE BASICALLY WASTING YOUR TIME IN NEW YORK WHEN EVERYTHING WE NEED FOR THEFACEBOOK IS RIGHT HERE IN SILICON VALLEY.

MARK, NEW YORK'S ALSO A IMPORTANT CENTER FOR THINGS A START-UP COMPANY LIKE US NEEDS - LIKE ADVERTISING AND BANKING CONTACTS.

YEAH. SURE.

HERE. LET ME TALK TO HIM.

HEY, EDUARDO! MAN RELAX. THINGS ARE GOING GREAT. I'VE GOT THESE TWO BIG INVESTORS I'M GOING TO INTRODUCE TO MARK.

THEY'RE READY TO PUT UP REAL MONEY AND IF THEY LIKE MARK, SOME BIG THINGS SHOULD HAPPEN REALLY FAST.

I'VE EXPLAINED THIS TO YOU BEFORE, PARKER! I'M RUNNING THE BUSINESS SIDE OF THEFACEBOOK! ANY MEETINGS WITH INVESTORS WILL HAVE TO INCLUDE ME!

WHAT THE HELL ARE YOU DOING SETTING UP THESE SORTS OF MEETINGS ANYWAY? IT'S NOT EVEN MARK'S JOB TO BE LOOKING FOR POTENTIAL INVESTORS - AND YOU'RE NOT DIRECTLY INVOLVED AT ALL! YOU'RE A HOUSEGUEST! THAT'S IT! A FUCKING HOUSEGUEST!

After hanging up the phone, Eduardo decided to bang out a letter explaining the reasons for his frustration.

The letter was to remind Mark of their business relationship. He reminded him of the agreement they'd made when they started thefacebook, that Eduardo was in charge of the business side of the company. Furthermore, Eduardo added that since he owned 30 percent of the company, he had the power to keep them from accepting any financial deals that he didn't agree with. Eduardo finished by saying that Mark had to accept this reality and he demanded written confirmation from Mark that he could run the business side of things as he saw fit.

Eduardo knew as soon as he sent the letter that it wasn't something a guy like Mark would react well to. But he felt he had to be as clear as possible. He realized Sean had taken them to some cool parties - maybe even gotten Mark laid with a Victoria's Secret model. But in Eduardo's view, he wasn't a part of thefacebook.

Eduardo was still the CFO. He'd put up the money that had made thefacebook possible. He was still the one funding their adventure in California. So, even though he was in New York, he believed he was still supposed to be calling the shots.

Mark's reaction to the letter as evidenced by the messages he left, were not what Eduardo expected.

YOU REALLY NEED TO MOVE OUT HERE, MAN. IT'S GREAT OUT HERE.

EVERYTHING'S GOING GREAT WITH THE COMPANY. THERE'S NO REASON TO ARGUE ABOUT THINGS THAT DON'T MATTER ANYWAY.

When Eduardo called Mark back, things went from bad to worse.

YEAH, MAN. SEAN AND I MET THOSE TWO INVESTORS I WAS TELLING YOU ABOUT.

THEY'RE WILLING TO MAKE AN ANGEL INVESTMENT AND GIVE US THE MONEY WE NEED TO KEEP GROWING AT THE CRAZY PACE WE'VE BEEN.

YOU KNOW HOW IT IS. WE NEED THE MONEY, SINCE THEFACEBOOK IS STARTING TO FALL INTO SERIOUS DEBT. WE'RE GOING TO NEED MORE SERVERS TO HANDLE ALL THE NEW PEOPLE AND TRAFFIC.

SOON WE'RE GOING TO HAVE TO HIRE MORE PEOPLE TO HANDLE THE INCREASED TRAFFIC.

MARK! I GET THAT! BUT YOU'RE MISSING THE POINT! YOU COMPLETELY BLEW OFF MY LETTER! YOU'RE TAKING BUSINESS MEETINGS WITHOUT ME THERE!

IT'S LIKE YOU'RE NOT JUST STEPPING ON MY TOES! I FEEL LIKE YOU AND SEAN ARE TRYING TO CUT OFF MY FEET!

WHAT THE HELL?! DID HE THINK I WAS JUST BLOWING OFF STEAM?! HIS ATTITUDE'S REALLY PISSING ME OFF! THEY'RE OUT THERE, LIVING IT UP ON MY DIME!

THE HOUSE IN CALIFORNIA! THE COMPUTER EQUIPMENT! THE SERVERS! IT'S ALL COMING OUT OF MY BANK ACCOUNT! MY OWN PERSONAL FUNDS!

I'M PAYING FOR EVERYTHING! AND HE'S GONNA TREAT ME LIKE AN ANGRY GIRLFRIEND THAT HE DOESN'T GIVE A SHIT ABOUT ANYMORE?!

Eduardo was determined to send a real message. One that Mark wouldn't be able to ignore.

So it was that three days later – on July 28, 2004 – that Eduardo made a decision that would change his life forever.

WHAT CAN I DO FOR YOU, SIR?

I WANT TO FREEZE MY BANK ACCOUNT. AND CANCEL ALL EXISTING CHECKS AND LINES OF CREDIT ATTACHED TO THIS ACCOUNT.

As the banker began the process, Eduardo feels a burst of adrenaline go through him. He knows he is crossing a line. But this was going to send Mark a real message, let him know how serious Eduardo is.

He feels it's Mark's own fault that he has the ability to do this anyway. Mark never bothered with the paperwork that would have made him a co-signatory on the account. Of course, Mark had never put a cent of his own money into the company, either. He'd been perfectly content to live off of Eduardo's funds, like Eduardo was his personal banker.

Only now, Mark had started to make decisions without Eduardo's involvement and Eduardo had to let him know that simply wasn't okay. Eduardo had to remind Mark what it meant to be a good partner and that thefacebook was a combined effort.

For a split-second, right before the banker hit the key that would freeze the account, he wonders if he's going too far.

That thought is then replaced by the thought of Mark and Sean running around California in Sean's BMW, taking meetings with investors, laughing at his concerns and protests while they lived it up on his dime.

They wouldn't be laughing when they tried to cash the next blank check – that was for sure.

OKAY, SIR. THE ACCOUNT'S FROZEN. PLEASE LET US KNOW IF AND WHEN YOU WISH TO REACTIVATE IT.

I WILL. THANK YOU.

Despite Eduardo's actions, two weeks later Sean and Mark found themselves in an elevator, on the way to a meeting that could launch them into a partnership that would change the face of the internet itself.

If Sean was right, when they left they would be well on their way toward the billion-dollar payoff he'd envisioned when he first saw thefacebook at Stanford.

In just the few short weeks since they'd run into each other, Sean had gotten to know Mark pretty well. In addition to proving he was a genius who could help him reach the top again, he was genuinely beginning to like him.

He felt Mark was brilliant, ambitious and had a caustic sense of humor.

Sean learned that Mark was still a quiet, socially awkward person. He had taken Mark to several parties, but Mark had never seemed comfortable at any of them.

Indeed, Sean learned that Mark always seemed to be most comfortable and happiest when he was in front of his computer, sometimes for twenty hours a stretch.

He would occasionally go on a date with his girlfriend or for a long drive to relax, but otherwise, he was a coding machine. He lived, breathed and ate the company he created.

Sean felt he could not have asked for more from a fledgling entrepreneur.

Sometimes he had to remind himself the kid standing next to him was barely 20 years old.

But he felt Mark's focus was amazing and that's why he was confident they were ready for a meeting that could be a catalyst to the billion dollar payoff that had so far eluded him.

In a weird way, Sean felt he had Eduardo to thank for pushing things to a head so rapidly. He had thought it would take all summer for Mark to get to the point he was at now.

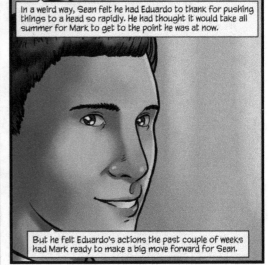

But he felt Eduardo's actions the past couple of weeks had Mark ready to make a big move forward for Sean.

I CAN'T BELIEVE HE'D SEND SUCH AN IDIOTIC LETTER MARK! IT'S LIKE A KIDNAPPER'S RANSOM LETTER REALLY!

I MEAN, HE MIGHT AS WELL HAVE WRITTEN IT IN CUT-OUT WORDS FROM NEWSPAPERS AND COLORED MAGAZINES!

HE'S GOING TO THREATEN AND MAKE DEMANDS ON YOU? THE KID HAS SOME SERIOUS SELF-AWARENESS ISSUES HE NEEDS TO DEAL WITH!

THE IDEA THAT HE THINKS HE'S RUNNING THE BUSINESS SIDE OF AN INTERNET COMPANY FROM NEW YORK WHILE EVERYONE'S OUT HERE IN CALIFORNIA IS ABSURD!

AND THEN HE'S GONNA TRY TO USE HIS 30 PERCENT OWNERSHIP OVER YOU LIKE IT'S A WEAPON - EDUARDO'S GONE RIGHT OFF HIS ROCKER!

I DON'T THINK THERE'S ANY NEED AT THIS POINT TO TURN THIS INTO ANYTHING MORE THAN EDUARDO MAKING A DESPERATE AND CHILDISH PLEA TO BE MORE INVOLVED WITH THE COMPANY.

I CAN ACCEPT THAT AND UNDERSTAND THAT.

But before things could be worked out, Eduardo had crossed a line that Mark and Sean would find difficult to forgive or forget.

I DON'T BELIEVE IT! HE FROZE THE ACCOUNT, MAN! HE JUST CUT YOU AND DUSTIN OFF AT THE THROAT! HE JUST TOOK A SHOT AT THE SOUL OF YOUR COMPANY!

I DON'T KNOW IF YOU REALIZE IT OR NOT, BUT WHAT EDUARDO JUST DID CAN EASILY DESTROY EVERYTHING YOU'VE WORKED ON. BECAUSE WITHOUT MONEY, THE COMPANY CAN'T FUNCTION.

IF THE SERVERS GO DOWN FOR EVEN ONE DAY, IT COULD PERMANENTLY HARM FACEBOOK'S REPUTATION.

USERS ARE FICKLE. FRIENDSTER AND OTHER SITES HAVE PROVEN THAT TIME AND TIME AGAIN. IF PEOPLE START TO LEAVE THE WEBSITE, THAT COULD PROVE DISASTROUS.

EVEN IF JUST A FEW PEOPLE LEAVE, IT COULD EVENTUALLY HAVE SEVERE REPERCUSSIONS, BECAUSE ALL OF THE USERS ARE INTER-CONNECTED.

COLLEGE KIDS ARE ONLINE BECAUSE THEIR FRIENDS ARE ONLINE. IF ONE DOMINO GOES, OTHERS ARE SURE TO FOLLOW.

I THINK EDUARDO DIDN'T REALIZE WHAT HE WAS DOING. I THINK HE ACTED OUT OF ANGER AND FRUSTRATION.

OKAY. POINT BLANK. I THINK IT WAS A CHILDISH STUNT THAT MAKES IT DIFFICULT FOR HIM TO BE A HUGE PART OF THIS COMPANY GOING FORWARD.

REALLY, MARK. IT WAS THE ACT OF A CHILD - NOT THIS BIG BUSINESSMAN HE TRIES TO PRESENT HIMSELF AS.

IT'S LIKE HE WAS A LITTLE KID ON THE PLAYGROUND, SCREAMING AT US, "IF YOU DON'T DO THINGS MY WAY, I'M TAKING MY TOYS AND GOING HOME."

OKAY. I GET IT. EDUARDO'S TAKEN HIS TOYS. TELL ME WHAT I NEED TO DO TO MAKE SURE HE DOESN'T TAKE THEM AGAIN.

With Sean's guidance, Mark reincorporated his company so they could begin the restructuring that Sean told him would be necessary to raise the money the company needed to go forward.

In order to keep thefacebook alive in the meantime, Mark took money he had saved up for tuition and came up with enough money to keep the servers running.

However, with its rapid growth, it became obvious Mark could no longer ignore the fact that his company was headed toward real financial trouble.

To make their situation more dire, Mark had recently received a legal letter from the Winklevoss twins, the first step in the initiation of a lawsuit.

LOOK, THE WINKLEVOSSES ARE A NUISANCE. THEY PRESENT NO REAL DANGER TO THIS COMPANY. I FEEL THEIR CLAIMS ARE UNFOUNDED AND OVERBLOWN.

HOWEVER, IF THEY GO THROUGH WITH THIS, IT'S GOING TO COST YOU OVER $200,000 JUST TO DEFEND YOURSELF.

WHICH MEANS WE NEED TO RAISE SOME MONEY PRETTY FAST.

SEEING AS HOW I DON'T WANT TO SELL THIS COMPANY YET AND I KNOW YOU DON'T EITHER, WE NEED TO FIND AN ANGEL INVESTMENT TO TIDE US OVER UNTIL WE CAN REACH A VALUATION THAT'LL MAKE ALL THESE ISSUES SEEM PETTY AND INSIGNIFICANT.

SEE WHAT YOU CAN DO.

So Sean did what he did best - he made a connection.

HEY, PETER! IT'S SEAN! LISTEN, I HAVE SOMETHING I WANT TO RUN BY YOU.

Which brings us to Mark and Sean riding in the elevator of a 52-story San Francisco skyscraper, with Mark knowing he only has to ace an imminent meeting and thefacebook would be on its way to what he knew it could be.

YOU KNOW THEY FILMED "TOWERING INFERNO" HERE, RIGHT?

THAT'S COMFORTING.

PETER'S GOING TO LOVE YOU. FIFTEEN MINUTES. THAT'S ALL IT'S GOING TO TAKE.

Peter Thiel, the man they were moments from meeting, was even more impressive and legendary than the building they were in.

Thiel was the founding force behind the very successful company PayPal, head of the multibillion-dollar venture fund Clarium Capital, a former chess master and one of the richest men in the country.

He was intimidating, fast-talking and a true genius - but Sean knew he was also exactly the sort of angel investor who had the guts and foresight to understand how important and groundbreaking thefacebook had the potential to be.

Because Thiel, like Sean and Mark, was more than just another entrepreneur - he saw himself as a revolutionary.

What most excited Sean was that he knew Thiel was the kind of guy who was looking for the next big thing - and he knew Thiel was especially interested in social networking.

Though they had never met before, Sean had helped get Thiel invested in Friendster - and he'd always kept the former PayPal CEO in the back of his mind in case another opportunity arose.

Now it had, and Sean was sure that if Thiel liked what Mark had to say the beginning of thefacebook as a true revolution would start.

Peter Thiel turned out to be everything Sean had warned Mark he would be - scary as hell, brilliant and willing to play ball.

HELLO, SIR.

After a short 15-minute pitch and an afternoon going over the details, Thiel announced he had made a decision.

HOW DOES FIVE HUNDRED THOUSAND DOLLARS SOUND?

With those words, the promise of a future for a company that Mark had started in a Harvard dorm room became reality and thefacebook was now officially on it's way.

Actually the company was now going to be simply known as Facebook. Sean had finally gotten Mark to slice off the "the" in the company's name, as part of the reorganization that was now an inevitability, a necessary step in getting the five-hundred thousand dollar "angel" investment that was going to solve their immediate issues and get them on the path they wanted to travel.

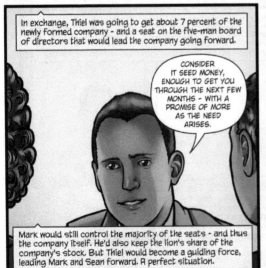

In exchange, Thiel was going to get about 7 percent of the newly formed company - and a seat on the five-man board of directors that would lead the company going forward.

CONSIDER IT SEED MONEY, ENOUGH TO GET YOU THROUGH THE NEXT FEW MONTHS - WITH A PROMISE OF MORE AS THE NEED ARISES.

Mark would still control the majority of the seats - and thus the company itself. He'd also keep the lion's share of the company's stock. But Thiel would become a guiding force, leading Mark and Sean forward. A perfect situation.

It was an overwhelming moment for both of them. Yet Sean knew some intense moments were coming down the road.

Thiel and he had both agreed during their meeting that reincorporating Facebook was necessary. It had to shed it's dorm room beginnings and morph into a new status.

They were going to have to reissue shares to represent the new setup, to include Thiel and of course Sean himself - who'd been working as a partner to Mark since he'd moved into the house anyway - and Dustin and Chris.

Which, of course, left the question of how to handle Eduardo. It was a subject Sean had discussed with Mark a few days earlier.

I STILL THINK HE DESERVES HIS 30 PERCENT.

FINE. I CAN LIVE WITH THAT. WE'LL STILL INVOLVE HIM AS MUCH AS HE WANTS TO BE INVOLVED.

BUT MARK, THIS NEW CORPORATION WE'RE TALKING ABOUT WILL HAVE DIFFERENT RULES - IT HAS TO HAVE DIFFERENT RULES.

THERE JUST ISN'T ANY WAY WE'RE GOING TO BE ABLE TO RUN THIS THE WAY WE WANT WITHOUT THE ABILITY TO ISSUE MORE SHARES AS THE SITUATION EVOLVES.

GOING FORWARD, PEOPLE HAVE TO BE GIVEN SHARES BASED ON THE AMOUNT OF WORK THEY DO FOR THE COMPANY.

THIS ISN'T SOME DORM ROOM PROJECT ANYMORE. IF ALL GOES WELL, THIS IS GOING TO BE A REAL COMPANY WITH A REAL INVESTOR. PEOPLE HAVE TO BE REIMBURSED PROPERLY.

OTHERWISE IT'S GOING TO BE IMPOSSIBLE TO CREATE A REAL VALUATION BASED ON WHAT FACEBOOK ACHIEVES.

THIS MEANS THAT IF DUSTIN, YOU AND I ARE DOING WHAT WE NEED TO DO TO MAKE THE COMPANY SUCCESSFUL, WE GET ISSUED MORE SHARES.

IF EDUARDO'S IN NEW YORK FINDING US MORE ADVERTISERS, THEN HE'LL GET REWARDED ACCORDINGLY.

BUT IF HE DOESN'T PRODUCE, HE'LL BE DILUTED JUST LIKE EVERYONE ELSE. HECK IF WE NEED TO RAISE MONEY, WE'LL ALL BE DILUTED!

I JUST WANT TO MAKE IT CLEAR, MARK. I FEEL WHAT EDUARDO DID WAS A HORRIBLE THING. HE THREATENED THIS COMPANY AT IT'S MOST FRAGILE STAGE.

I KNOW. BUT I CAN'T BLAME HIM FOR IT.

I KNOW, MARK. I DON'T THINK YOU'RE CAPABLE OF HATING ANYONE. BUT I THINK HE'S SHOWN US WHERE HE STANDS. TO US, FACEBOOK IS OUR EVERYTHING - IT'S OUR LIVES.

FOR EXAMPLE, I CAN TELL RIGHT NOW YOU'RE NOT GOING BACK TO HARVARD WHEN THE SUMMER'S OVER. YOU CARE TOO MUCH ABOUT FACEBOOK.

BUT I KNOW EDUARDO WILL NEVER QUIT SCHOOL. HE'S NOT GOING TO GIVE UP EVERYTHING FOR FACEBOOK. YOU KNOW WHY? BECAUSE YOU'VE FOUND YOUR PLACE IN THE WORLD AND HE HASN'T.

Mark thought about their momentous meeting with Thiel.

THERE'S GOING TO BE A LOT OF CHANGES. ONE OF YOUR JOBS IS GOING TO BE GETTING EDUARDO TO AGREE TO THE LEGAL DETAILS. IT'S NOT PERSONAL. IT'S BUSINESS.

I'VE HAD A LOT OF SUCCESS AND I CAN TELL YOU BUSINESSES LIKE YOURS HAVE TWO DISTINCT STARTING POINTS.

THERE'S THE FIRST STARTING POINT: TWO KIDS IN A DORM ROOM HACKING AROUND ON A COMPUTER. THEN THERE'S THE SECOND STARTING POINT: HERE, IN A SKYSCRAPER IN DOWNTOWN SAN FRANCISCO.

YOU EXPERIENCE A SPARK OF GENIUS, A FLAME BURSTING UP OUT OF NOWHERE, A LIGHTNING BOLT OF IMAGINATION.

IF YOU'RE THERE IN THE DORM ROOM, YOU HAVE AN EXCITING AND WONDERFUL STORY TO TELL. YOU GET TO BE A PART OF SOMETHING COOL.

BUT IF YOU'RE HERE IN A SKYSCRAPER, WELL, THAT'S DIFFERENT. THIS IS THE REAL BEGINNING OF THE COMPANY WITH A CAPITAL C.

THIS IS THE REAL BUSINESS, THE CORPORATION, THE SECOND LIGHTNING BOLT THAT TAKES YOU STRAIGHT UP TO THE HEAVENS.

YEAH, IT'S NOT JUST TWO KIDS IN A DORM ROOM ANYMORE. IF EDUARDO CAN'T GET THAT, THEN HE DOESN'T REALLY CARE ABOUT FACEBOOK THE WAY WE DO.

THEN HE'S NO BETTER THAN THE WINKLEVOSSES, TRYING TO GRAB ONTO YOUR ANKLES AS YOU SOAR TOWARD THE HEAVENS.

YOU NEED TO MAKE THE RIGHT DECISION FOR THE COMPANY.

LET ME MAKE THIS CLEAR. NO INVESTOR IS GOING TO HAND YOU MONEY WITH SOME KID RUNNING AROUND NEW YORK, CLAIMING TO BE THE HEAD OF THE BUSINESS SIDE OF THE COMPANY, FLAUNTING SOME "30 PERCENT" OWNERSHIP STATUS, HOLDING IT OVER YOU LIKE A SABER READY TO CHOP OFF YOUR HEADS BY FREEZING YOUR BANK ACCOUNT, THREATENING YOU AND THREATENING FACEBOOK.

Sean could tell the future of Facebook was all Mark cared about now. After they filled out the necessary paperwork, Sean knew he was on top of something huge. This "Mark Zuckerberg Production" was going to change the world. Like Napster, but bigger - putting the real world on the internet.

FACEBOOK IS NOW READY TO GO TO THE NEXT LEVEL. TELL YOU WHAT. WHEN WE GET TO THREE MILLION FACEBOOK MEMBERS, I'LL LET YOU TAKE MY 360 FERRARI SPYDER OUT FOR A DRIVE.

WITH THIS 500 GRAND IN SEED MONEY, YOU CAN NOW BUILD FACEBOOK HOWEVER YOU WANT. AS BIG AS YOU CAN DREAM. JUST DO ME ONE FAVOR, OKAY?

SURE. ANYTHING.

DON'T FUCK IT UP.

Sean wasn't worried. He knew Mark wasn't going to let anyone fuck Facebook up. He had a revolution he was born to lead - no matter what the cost.

By October, 2004, Mark and the rest of the Facebook crew had been kicked out of their La Jennifer Way sublet in suburban Palo Alto after complaints for climbing on their roof, playing their music too loud and throwing their patio furniture into their pool, among other things.

So, it was that when Eduardo came down for a visit for the first time since freezing Facebook's bank account, he couldn't help but smile. Facebook's new headquarters in Los Altos, California, had plenty of hardware, but still had the feel of a college dorm.

Which was the whole idea. Despite the increasing amount of money and lawyers, Mark did not want to lose the college feel of the company. To him, it would always be a college experiment that exploded. It was a sentiment that Eduardo - who had finally accepted that Mark was going to do things his way - realized he shared.

Mark had been really angry about the bank account being frozen. Likewise Eduardo wasn't pleased about Mark continuing with investor meetings and was even jealous that Mark had gotten the major financing from Thiel without him present. But they eventually came to an understanding.

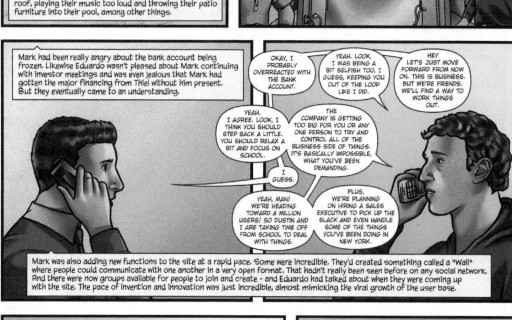

OKAY, I PROBABLY OVERREACTED WITH THE BANK ACCOUNT.

YEAH. LOOK, I WAS BEING A BIT SELFISH TOO, I GUESS, KEEPING YOU OUT OF THE LOOP LIKE I DID.

HEY LET'S JUST MOVE FORWARD FROM NOW ON. THIS IS BUSINESS. BUT WE'RE FRIENDS. WE'LL FIND A WAY TO WORK THINGS OUT.

YEAH. I AGREE. LOOK, I THINK YOU SHOULD STEP BACK A LITTLE. YOU SHOULD RELAX A BIT AND FOCUS ON SCHOOL.

THE COMPANY IS GETTING TOO BIG FOR YOU OR ANY ONE PERSON TO TRY AND CONTROL ALL OF THE BUSINESS SIDE OF THINGS. IT'S BASICALLY IMPOSSIBLE, WHAT YOU'VE BEEN DEMANDING.

I GUESS.

YEAH, MAN! WE'RE HEADING TOWARD A MILLION USERS! SO DUSTIN AND I ARE TAKING TIME OFF FROM SCHOOL TO DEAL WITH THINGS.

PLUS, WE'RE PLANNING ON HIRING A SALES EXECUTIVE TO PICK UP THE SLACK AND EVEN HANDLE SOME OF THE THINGS YOU'VE BEEN DOING IN NEW YORK.

Mark was also adding new functions to the site at a rapid pace. Some were incredible. They'd created something called a "Wall" where people could communicate with one another in a very open format. That hadn't really been seen before on any social network. And there were now groups available for people to join and create - and Eduardo had talked about when they were coming up with the site. The pace of invention and innovation was just incredible, almost mimicking the viral growth of the user base.

Eduardo got a sense of how big Facebook had become when his first week back at school, when he had heard that President Summers had announced to the entering freshmen that he had checked them all out on Facebook.

He thought it was incredible that the president of Harvard was using their site to get to know the incoming class only 10 months after they'd created it.

So he was feeling good when he got a phone call from Mark.

YEAH, MAN. WE NEED YOU TO COME OUT AND SIGN SOME PAPERS. IT'S INCORPORATION PAPERS AND STUFF THAT DEALS WITH THE RESTRUCTURING OF THE COMPANY NOW THAT THIEL'S ON BOARD.

SURE. WHY NOT? SOUNDS LIKE IT'S ALL FOR THE BEST.

As Eduardo received and then read the documents he'd come out to sign, he found the legislation confusing. First, there were two common-stock purchase agreements - essentially allowing him to "buy" stock in the newly reincorporated "Facebook", instead of the now-worthless "stock" he had in the old "thefacebook".

Second, there was an exchange agreement, for exchanging his old shares of thefacebook for new shares in the new company. Lastly, there was a holder voting agreement - something Eduardo didn't entirely understand, but seemed like more legalese than was necessary for the company to function.

AFTER THE REPURCHASES AND EXCHANGES, YOU'LL HAVE A TOTAL OF 1,328,334 SHARES OF THE NEW COMPANY.

THAT MEANS YOU'LL HAVE 34.4 PERCENT OF OWNERSHIP OF FACEBOOK RIGHT NOW.

THE RISE IN YOUR PERCENTAGE FROM YOUR ORIGINAL 30 PERCENT IS DUE TO THE NECESSITY, IN THE FUTURE, OF DILUTION AS THE COMPANY HIRES MORE PEOPLE AND AWARDS OTHER INVESTORS THAT COME ALONG.

SO MY PERCENTAGE HAS GONE DOWN TO ABOUT 51 PERCENT, DUSTIN OWNS 6.81 PERCENT, SEAN OWNS 6.47 PERCENT AND THIEL GETS ABOUT 7 PERCENT.

Included in the documents was a vesting schedule that stated Eduardo wouldn't be able to sell his shares anytime soon. So, really, his ownership was still on paper - like everyone else he assumed. There was also a general release of any claims against Mark and Facebook. Basically, if he signed, he'd be saying that the new papers outlined his position at Facebook in it's entirety. In other words, everything that came before would be history.

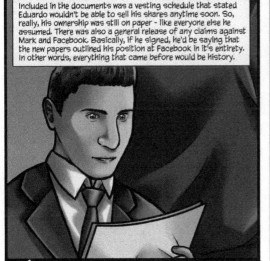

What meant the most to Eduardo is that after all the rancor of the past few months, these papers seemed to say that he was just as big a part of the company as he'd ever been. Things might change a bit going forward as more money came in and more people were hired, but he was being told that this was just a necessary restructuring.

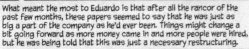

ANYWAY, PETER'S GOING TO THROW A REAL COOL PARTY WHEN WE HIT ONE MILLION MEMBERS, AT HIS RESTAURANT IN SAN FRANCISCO. YOU'LL DEFINITELY WANT TO MAKE IT BACK OUT FOR THAT.

THESE PAPERS ARE IMPORTANT AND SIGNING THEM WILL BE A BIG STEP FORWARD FOR FACEBOOK.

Eduardo was still a bit confused by the legalese, but he felt protected. First, because Facebook's lawyers were there - which meant, in his mind, that they were his lawyers as well. More importantly, his friend Mark was there, telling him these documents were necessary and good.

JUST A NECESSARY RESTRUCTURING AND SOME LEGAL PAPERWORK THAT HAS TO BE DONE, RIGHT? EVERYTHING'S GOING TO WORK OUT JUST FINE.

ONE MILLION MEMBERS ALREADY? YEAH, I'M DEFINITELY COMING BACK OUT FOR THAT!

HEY! I OWN 34 PERCENT OF FACEBOOK! GIVE ME A PEN! WHEN I'M DONE WE'LL ALL GO OUT AND CELEBRATE!

It was December 3, 2004 when Eduardo entered Facebook's Millionth Member Party. He thought it was impressive - and very Facebook. Most of those in attendance were hip, cool and college-aged.

The party was going pretty well for him. He was telling everyone that would listen that he had co-founded Facebook along with Mark and Dustin. Some of the girls he talked to smiled and some looked at him like he was crazy. At Harvard, everyone knew what he had done. Out here, they were looking at Mark - and only Mark.

Eduardo would join his friends eventually, but thought that the way things were going, he was going to be part of one of the biggest businesses in history - so he should enjoy his anonymity while he still could. Plus, he was experiencing culture shock. Everything seemed foreign to him because it was all happening blindingly fast.

Of course, Eduardo knew that the moment he'd stepped out of his cab and found himself between Mark's Infiniti and Parker's BMW - while glancing at Thiel's Ferrari Spyder. Eduardo chuckled a bit when he realized that he still lived in a dorm room and walked to his classes. It was proof that things had happened - and were still happening - pretty fast.

Yeah, things had changed pretty dramatically over the summer. That realization made him second-guess his decision to stay in New York. But it was okay. It was a choice he had made. He had nobody to fault but himself. He could have taken time off from school. He quickly put the thought out of his head. He was a senior now, only five months until graduation. Then he could throw himself into Facebook like the rest. For now, he had a drink to get and a cute girl to talk to. Everything was going to be just fine.

Sean was smiling, because everything was going according to plan. Catching sight of Eduardo chatting up a cute girl, he was happy everything had gone so smoothly. Peter and Mark were a great match and Eduardo had signed the necessary legal papers and had executed the restructuring agreements.

Peter had given them the money they needed to keep flying forward. Facebook had passed a million users and they were adding tens of thousands more a week. Pretty soon, they'd be opening it up to more schools, more campuses. Eventually maybe even high schools. After that - who knows? Maybe Facebook would one day be open to everyone. Exclusivity had already worked it's magic. People trusted Facebook. People loved Facebook. People were going to want to pay billions for Facebook.

One million members had suddenly become two and they were already close to three. Facebook was simply everywhere. On 500 campuses, in seemingly every newspaper and on virtually every news show. No. Facebook wasn't the real world. It was way bigger than that and Eduardo was proud of what Mark and he had done.

It was April 3, 2005 and it would only be two months until Eduardo graduated Harvard and entered the real world - though he wasn't sure what that meant anymore. It certainly didn't describe Facebook's new offices in Palo Alto, where Mark was building Facebook ten thousand users at a time. The real world didn't have anything to do with Facebook, because the real world simply didn't move that fast.

Oddly enough, despite the rapid rate at which the company was growing, he had had almost no interaction with the California crew in two months - except for an odd phone call or odd request for a contact from New York. Finally, Mark had gotten back in touch via e-mail 2 days ago, asking him to come out for an important business meeting and to train a new hire.

In the e-mail, Mark had also mentioned something that had caused Eduardo a little bit of concern. Seems two prestigious venture capital funds were interested in Facebook and here was a chance they'd let one of them invest. Furthermore, Mark noted Dustin, Sean and he were thinking about selling their stock if the deal went through - two million dollars apiece - Mark estimated in the e-mail.

Eduardo was a little surprised at that. First, from the papers he'd signed, he was pretty certain he didn't have the ability to sell stock - his shares didn't vest for a long, long time. So why were Mark, Sean and Dustin able to cash out two million dollars' worth? Hadn't they signed the same papers he had, during the restructure? And second, why was Mark talking about selling shares at all? Since when did Mark care about money? And why did Sean Parker get to make two million bucks when he'd been a part of the company officially for about ten weeks? Eduardo had been there since the beginning. It certainly didn't seem fair.

Eduardo was sure he was simply misunderstanding the situation and that Mark would clear things up when he got to California. No matter what, he decided he was going to keep his emotions in check. Since his anger had only hurt him during the summer he was determined to be calm, rational and understanding. Yes. Tomorrow, he would fly out, check out the new offices, attend a business meeting and train that new hire.

He hoped it would be the beginning of things going back to normal between him and Mark, so that when he graduated he could go back to his old role as Mark's founding partner. The thought brought a smile to his face. Yes, tomorrow he'd be back with Mark - and Mark would explain everything.

The next day was a day Eduardo will remember for the rest of his life. Immediately upon entering Facebook's fancy new office, a lawyer greeted him with more contracts to sign.

At first, he thought the guy was joking. He hadn't even had a chance to check out the place, ask Mark about the new hire or inquire about the two-million-dollar stock sale. But as soon as he started reading the legalese, he realized this trip wasn't about a business meeting.

This was an ambush. The full realization of what Eduardo was reading struck him like a gunshot to the chest, shattering him from the inside out destroying a part of him that he knew he'd never get back. Nothing could describe what it felt like - because even though he should have seen it coming he simply hadn't.

HOW COULD I HAVE BEEN SO BLIND? SO FUCKING STUPID?

He simply hadn't expected it from Mark - from his friend, from he kid he'd met when they were two geeks in a underground Jewish fraternity trying to fit in at Harvard. They'd had their problems and Mark had the ability to be pretty cold and distant - but this was way beyond that. To Eduardo, this was a betrayal - pure and simple.

First, there was a document dated January 14, 2005 - a written consent of TheFacebook to increase the number of shares the company was authorized to issue up to 19 million common shares. Then, there was a second action dated March 28, issuing up to 20,890,000 shares. And then there was a document allowing the issuance of 3.3 million additional shares to Mark Zuckerberg, 2 million additional shares to Dustin Moskovitz and over 2 million additional shares to Sean Parker.

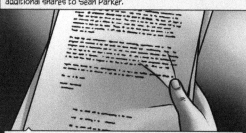

Eduardo stared at the numbers, rapidly doing the calculations in his head. With all the new shares, his ownership of Facebook was no longer anywhere near 34 percent. If just the new shares had been issued to Mark, Sean and Dustin, he was down to well below 10 percent - and if all the authorized new shares were issued, he'd be diluted down to almost nothing.

They were diluting him out of the company.

THESE NEW SHARES ARE NECESSARY.

THERE ARE INTERESTED VCS WHO WILL NEED THEM.

YOUR SIGNATURE IS A FORMALITY. THE SHARES HAVE BEEN AUTHORIZED ANYWAY. IT'S GOOD AND NECESSARY FOR THE COMPANY.

NO! NO!

I REFUSE TO SIGN AWAY MY OWNERSHIP OF FACEBOOK! I REFUSE TO SIGN AWAY MY ACCOMPLISHMENT!

I WAS THERE IN THE BEGINNING! I WAS IN THAT DORM ROOM WITH MARK! I AM A FOUNDER OF FACEBOOK AND I DESERVE MY 30 PERCENT! MARK AND I HAD AN AGREEMENT!

The lawyer's response was immediate.

YOU ARE NO LONGER A MEMBER OF FACEBOOK.

YOU ARE NO LONGER PART OF THE MANAGEMENT TEAM, NO LONGER AN EMPLOYEE - NO LONGER CONNECTED IN ANY WAY. YOU WILL BE EXPUNGED FROM THE CORPORATE HISTORY.

TO MARK ZUCKERBERG AND FACEBOOK, EDUARDO SAVERIN NO LONGER EXISTS.

I CAN'T BELIEVE WHAT I'M HEARING! I CAN'T BELIEVE THIS BETRAYAL!

YOU HAVE NO CHOICE. THE DECISION HAS BEEN MADE BY MARK ZUCKERBERG, THE FOUNDER AND CEO, AND BY THE NEW PRESIDENT OF FACEBOOK.

WHO THE HELL IS THE NEW PRESIDENT OF FACEBOOK?

When he thought about it, he realized he already knew the answer.

Soon after his promotion, Sean helped swing a deal in which Accel Partners was going to invest close to $13 million for a small stake in the company - an investment that would put Facebook's valuation at close to $100 million.

ONE HUNDRED MILLION DOLLARS, MAN! AND THAT'S JUST A START! I GUARANTEE YOU WE'LL TRIPLE THAT VALUATION IN THE NEXT SIX MONTHS! AND BY THE END OF THE YEAR WE'RE ON TARGET TO HAVE 50 MILLION USERS!

WE'RE ABOUT TO GIVE BIRTH TO A BILLION-DOLLAR BABY, MY FRIEND - AND IT'S GONNA BE FUCKING AWESOME!

Of course., the manic energy and insatiable appetite to get what he wanted - the attitude that yearned to make Facebook as big as Google and Microsoft - had a downside as well. Eduardo had always said Sean was like a comet tearing through the atmosphere. He'd already burned through two start-ups. His question to Mark had never been "if" he'd burn through Facebook as well, but when.

I NEVER EVEN HEARD THE SIRENS!

OFFICERS, THERE MUST BE SOME MISTAKE. THIS IS JUST A SOCIAL GATHERING. RIGHT OUTSIDE A COLLEGE CAMPUS. JUST PURE, INNOCENT FUN. HARMLESS. NOTHING MUCH GOING ON AT ALL.

OKAY, SO MAYBE THERE'S ALCOHOL IN THE HOUSE. AND MAYBE THE MUSIC'S A BIT TOO LOUD. AND, UH, MAYBE SOME OF THE KIDS WERE DOING POT AND COKE.

I DON'T KNOW, GUYS. I'VE SPENT ALL MY TIME ON THE DANCE FLOOR - AND OTHER THAN THE INHALER IN MY PANTS POCKET AND THE EPIPEN FULL OF EPINEPHRINE IN MY SHIRT, I'M CLEAN AS A NEWBORN. MY CHRONIC ASTHMA AND RIDICULOUS FUCKING ALLERGIES MAKE SURE OF THAT.

WHO CARES, ANYWAY? IT'S A PARTY! THERE'S A BUNCH OF COLLEGE KIDS HERE - AND ISN'T COLLEGE SUPPOSED TO BE ABOUT EXPERIMENTATION? REVOLUTION? FREEDOM?

CONSIDERING OUR LOCALE, DO YOU THINK YOU GUYS CAN FIND IT IN YOUR HEARTS TO BE A TAD FORGIVING?

Sean couldn't believe his bad luck and bad timing. Then, he thought it might be more than that. Maybe, just maybe, as Facebook got bigger than big, as the money poured in and the VCs started to think in terms of billions - maybe there were people who felt they didn't need Sean Parker anymore. It had happened twice before. Could it be happening again? Or was he being paranoid?

GUESS NOT, HUH?

Sean knew he had to inform Mark about his misfortune immediately. Speculation could do a lot of damage and - innocent or not - it didn't exactly look good for the president of a transformative, world-changing, billion-dollar company to get busted with an undergraduate employee at a house party. He didn't think he was going to end up in jail - but he was certain of one thing. Innocent or not, setup or pure bad luck, Mark Zuckerberg was going to be pretty pissed off.

CAN I MAKE A PHONE CALL?

At some point, Mark found out what had happened. He felt the information he had received had to be dealt with quickly - and utter efficiency. Sean Parker was a genius. He'd been instrumental in getting Facebook to where it was now. Sean Parker was one of Mark's heroes, and would always be a mentor, an adviser and a friend.

But after hearing the details of a house party that had been busted by the cops, he came to a quick decision: Sean Parker had to go. Whatever the reason, even though Sean wasn't going to be tried or indicted for anything he'd done - in some people's minds the current situation would make Sean a danger to Facebook.

To his detractors, he had always been unpredictable and wild - people didn't always understand him and some found his energy level terrifying. But this was different. This was black and white. No matter why it had happened - whether it was bad luck, or something else - the result was as clear as data in, data out. Sean Parker had to go.

Like Eduardo, like the Winklevosses, anything that became a threat - no matter the intention - had to be dealt with, because in the end, the only thing that mattered was Facebook. It was Mark Zuckerberg's creation, his baby - and it had become the focus of his life. In the beginning, maybe it had simply been something fun, something interesting.

But now, Facebook was an extension of the only love of Mark's life - the computer with that glowing screen in front of his face. And like the personal computer that Mark's idol Bill Gates had unleashed on humanity by means of his groundbreaking software, Facebook was a revolution, too - world changing, creating a free exchange of information across social networks that would digitize the world in a way nothing else would. Mark wouldn't let anything - or anyone - stand in the way of Facebook.

What Mark Zuckerberg had become could best be illustrated by the business card, simple and elegant, with a single sentence printed across the center, that he created - the business card he printed out to carry with him everywhere. In one sense, the card represented nothing more than Mark Zuckerberg's personal brand of humor. But in another sense, the card was more than a joke - because it was true.

No matter what else anyone wanted to believe, no matter what anyone else ever tried to do, the sentiment of the card would always be true. Inevitably, indelibly, indubitably, undeniably true.

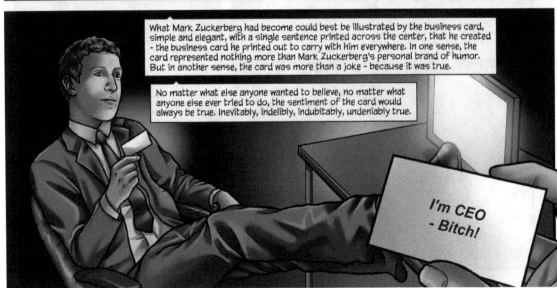

I'm CEO - Bitch!

CPSIA information can be obtained
at www.ICGtesting.com
Printed in the USA
BVHW011716020921
615786BV00034B/262